Math
Activity Book

Book Staff and Contributors

Lisa White   *Lead Content Specialist*
Megan Simmons   *Content Specialist*
Lauralyn Vaughn   *Manager, Instructional Design*
Susan Raley   *Text Editor*
Tricia Battipede   *Senior Creative Manager*
Jayoung Cho   *Senior Visual Designer*
Caitlin Gildrien   *Visual Designer*
Tricia Battipede, Mike Bohman, Shannon Palmer   *Cover Designers*
Deborah Benton, Dana Crisafulli, Michele Patrick, Maureen Steddin, Alisa Steel, David Stienecker   *Writers*
Amy Eward   *Senior Manager, Writers and Editors*
Abhilasha Parakh   *Senior Project Manager*

Doug McCollum   *Senior Vice President, Product Development*
Kristin Morrison   *Vice President, Design, Creative, and UX*
Rohit Lakhani   *Vice President, Program Management and Operations*
Kelly Engel   *Senior Director, Curriculum*
Christopher Frescholtz   *Senior Director, Program Management*
Erica Castle   *Director, Creative Services*
Lisa Dimaio Iekel   *Senior Production Manager*

Illustrations Credits

All illustrations © Stride, Inc. unless otherwise noted
Characters: Tommy DiGiovanni, Matt Fedor, Ben Gamache, Shannon Palmer
Cover: Elephant © ToprakBeyBetmen/iStock; Pastel wallpaper patterns © mxtama/iStock.
Interior Pattern: Pastel wallpaper patterns © mxtama/iStock.

At Stride, Inc. (NYSE: LRN)—formerly K12 Inc.—we are reimagining lifelong learning as a rich, deeply personal experience that prepares learners for tomorrow. Since its inception, Stride has been committed to removing barriers that impact academic equity and to providing high-quality education for anyone—particularly those in underserved communities. The company has transformed the teaching and learning experience for millions of people by providing innovative, high-quality, tech-enabled education solutions, curriculum, and programs directly to students, schools, the military, and enterprises in primary, secondary, and post-secondary settings. Stride is a premier provider of K-12 education for students, schools, and districts, including career learning services through middle and high school curriculum. Providing a solution to the widening skills gap in the workplace and student loan crisis, Stride equips students with real world skills for in-demand jobs with career learning. For adult learners, Stride delivers professional skills training in healthcare and technology, as well as staffing and talent development for Fortune 500 companies. Stride has delivered millions of courses over the past decade and serves learners in all 50 states and more than 100 countries. The company is a proud sponsor of the Future of School, a nonprofit organization dedicated to closing the gap between the pace of technology and the pace of change in education. More information can be found at stridelearning.com, K12.com, destinationsacademy.com, galvanize.com, techelevator.com, and medcerts.com.

ISBN: 978-1-60153-579-5

Printed by Walsworth, Saint Joseph, MI, USA, April 2023.

Table of Contents

Addition and Subtraction of Fractions

Addition and Subtraction of Mixed Numbers

Points on a Coordinate Plane

Measurement and Unit Conversion

Classification of Two-Dimensional Figures

Practice Evaluating an Expression

Parker evaluated an expression. Review his work.

$$36 \div 6 + (18 - 6 \times 2)$$
$$36 \div 6 + (18 - \mathbf{12})$$
$$36 \div 6 + \mathbf{6}$$
$$36 \div \mathbf{12}$$
$$3$$

1. Parker made a mistake. The correct value of the expression is 12.

   a. What mistake did Parker make?

   _____

   _____

   b. What should Parker have done differently?

   _____

   _____

   c. Correctly evaluate the expression $36 \div 6 + (18 - 6 \times 2)$.
      Show your work.

> Pssst . . . remember, parentheses first!

Evaluate the expression.

2. $32 - 2 \times 5$ _____

3. $\frac{15}{5} - 1 + 50 \div 5$ _____

4. $11 \times 3 + 16 \div 4 - 2$ _____

5. $74 + 12 - \frac{18}{3} \times 2 - 20$ _____

6. $(46 - 24) \div 2$ _____

7. $5 \times (12 - 7) + 23$ _____

8. $(6 - 5) \times (4 - 2) + \frac{12}{4}$ _____

9. $9 \times 3 + (32 \div 8 - 3) - 5$ _____

Using Grouping Symbols (B)

Practice Working with Nested Grouping Symbols

Follow the steps to evaluate the expression.

1. $[(3 + 17) - 4 \times 2] - [9 - (2 \times 2)]$

    a. Add 3 and 17. _____

    b. Multiply 4 by 2. _____

    c. Subtract 8 from 20. _____

    d. Multiply 2 by 2. _____

    e. Subtract 4 from 9. _____

    f. Subtract 5 from 12. _____

Evaluate the expression.

2. $65 + [(20 - 16) \times 5]$ _____

3. $100 - \{7 \times (5 - 2)\}$ _____

4. $2 \times \{56 \div (2 \times 4)\} - 18 \div 3$ _____

5. $\{15 - (3 + 7)\} \times (2 + 6)$ _____

6. $3 + [(4 + 6) - 7] - (1 + 2)$ _____

7. $[(17 - 8) \times 6] - [(12 + 15) \div 9]$ _____

8. $\{(32 \div 4) - (20 \div 4)\} \times 8$ _____

9. $48 \div 6 + [(25 - 13) \times (2 + 1)]$ _____

Using Grouping Symbols (C)

Practice Placing Grouping Symbols

Answer the questions.

1. The expression $8 \div 2 + 6 \times 9 - 7$ has a value of 51.

    a. Does the value of the expression change if parentheses are placed around $2 + 6$? If so, what is the new value of the expression?

    _____

    b. Does the value of the expression change if parentheses are placed around $9 - 7$? If so, what is the new value of the expression?

    _____

    c. Does the value of the expression change if parentheses are placed around $8 \div 2$? If so, what is the new value of the expression?

    _____

Place parentheses in the expression so that it has the given value.

2. $7 + 9 - 4 \times 3$
   Value: 22

3. $1 + 5 \div 2 + 3$
   Value: 2

Parentheses rock!

4. $5 \times 6 \div 3 + 2$
   Value: 6

5. $4 \times 6 - 4 - 8 \div 2$
   Value: 4

6. $3 + 6 \times 9 + 3$
   Value: 84

7. $5 + 3 - 12 \div 6 - 2$
   Value: 5

8. $8 + 9 \div 3 \times 6 - 5$
   Value: 11

9. $7 \times 5 - 10 + 6 \div 8$
   Value: 33

Solve.

10. On weekdays, Kiki walks 2 miles in the morning and 1 mile in the evening. On Saturdays, she walks 4 miles. Place parentheses in the expression to represent the number of miles Kiki walks each week.

    $5 \times 2 + 1 + 4$

Exploring Numerical Expressions (A)

Practice Translating an Expression from Words to Numbers

Two students translated the word phrase:
4 less than the quotient of 10 and 5

1. Marty's expression was $4 - 10 \div 5$. Frank's expression was $10 \div 5 - 4$.
   Which student wrote the correct expression? Explain how you know.

   _____

   _____

   _____

Translate the word phrase into a numerical expression.

2. 18 fewer than 42

   _____

3. the total of 153 and 21

   _____

4. 63 separated into 5 equal groups

   _____

5. the product of 9 and 4

   _____

6. 97 decreased by 45 then increased by 11

_____

7. 8 times 5 divided by 4

_____

8. 88 more than the quotient of 35 and 7

_____

9. the product of 6 and the sum of 4 and 5

_____

10. 45 divided by the difference 7 minus 2

_____

11. 10 times the quotient of 6 and 3

_____

12. the product of the sum of 3 and 6 and the sum of 2 and 7

_____

Exploring Numerical Expressions (B)

Practice Translating an Expression from Numbers to Words

Anya wrote a word phrase for the expression:
$35 - 16$

1. Anya's word phrase was "the difference of 16 and 35." Her phrase is incorrect.

   a. What mistake did Anya make?

   _____

   _____

   b. Write a correct word phrase to represent $35 - 16$.

   _____

   _____

Write a word phrase to represent the numerical expression.

2. $10 + 9$

   _____

3. $14 \div 2$

   _____

4. $11 \times 8 + 20$

_____

5. $2 \times (18 - 7)$

_____

Write a real-world problem to represent the numerical expression.

6. $15 - 3$

_____

_____

_____

_____

7. $(20 + 4) \div 6$

_____

_____

_____

_____

Powers of 10 (A)

Practice Representing Powers of 10

Answer the questions.

1. 10,000,000 is a power of 10 because 1 is followed only by zeros.

   a. How many zeros are in the number 10,000,000? _____

   b. A power of 10 has a base of 10 and an exponent. The exponent equals the number of zeros. Write 10,000,000 with a base of 10 and an exponent. _____

   c. A power of 10 can also be written as a product of factors of 10. The number of factors equals the number of zeros in the power of 10. Write 10,000,000 as a product of factors of 10.

   _____

Complete the table by writing each power of 10 as a base with an exponent and then as a product.

	Whole Number	Base and Exponent	Product
2.	100		
3.	1,000		
4.	10,000		
5.	100,000		
6.	1,000,000		

Write the power of 10 as a base with an exponent.

7. 100,000,000,000,000,000 _____

8. 100,000,000,000 _____

Write the number as a product.

9. 10^{10} _____

10. 10,000,000,000,000 _____

_____

Using an exponent is a shortcut for writing powers of 10.

Practice Multiplying by a Power of 10

Aisha determined that the product 40×100 was 400.

1. Aisha made a mistake.

   a. What mistake did Aisha make?

   _____

   _____

   b. What is the correct number of zeros in the product? Why?

   _____

   _____

   c. What is the correct product? _____

Explain how the powers of 10 can be used to find the product.

2. $19 \times 10,000$

   _____

3. $1,000 \times 159$

   _____

4. 70×10^5

   _____

5. $10^4 \times 8$ _____

6. $94 \times 1{,}000$ _____

7. $10{,}000 \times 126$ _____

8. 5×10^2 _____

9. 161×10^3 _____

10. 100×57 _____

Multidigit Whole Number Multiplication (A)

Practice Multiplying Whole Numbers

Follow the instructions to multiply 413 × 858.

1. Write your answers to each part in the appropriate box.

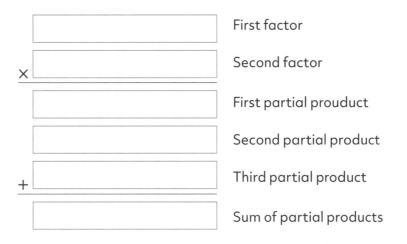

a. Write the problem vertically.

b. Find the first partial product. Multiply 8 by each digit in 413. Regroup as needed.

c. Find the second partial product. Write a 0 as a placeholder in the ones column. Then, multiply 5 by each digit in 413. Regroup as needed.

d. Find the third partial product. Write a 0 as a placeholder in the ones column and the tens column. Then, multiply 8 by each digit in 413. Regroup as needed.

e. Add the three partial products.

Multiply. Show your work.

2.
$$\begin{array}{r} 700 \\ \times\ 321 \\ \hline \end{array}$$

3.
$$\begin{array}{r} 3{,}000 \\ \times\ 181 \\ \hline \end{array}$$

4.
$$\begin{array}{r} 735 \\ \times\ 39 \\ \hline \end{array}$$

5.
$$\begin{array}{r} 9{,}715 \\ \times\ 78 \\ \hline \end{array}$$

6. $4{,}000 \times 60 =$ _____

7. $500 \times 35 =$ _____

8. $874 \times 66 =$ _____

9. $7{,}637 \times 542 =$ _____

Multidigit Whole Number Multiplication (B)

Practice Multiplying Whole Numbers in the Real World

A dictionary has 1,498 pages. Each page contains 25 definitions. Answer the questions.

1. Kiki determined that the dictionary contained 10,486 definitions. Review her work.

$$
\begin{array}{r}
\overset{2}{}\overset{1}{4}\overset{1}{9}8 \\
\times\ \ \ 25 \\
\hline
7{,}490 \\
+2{,}996 \\
\hline
10{,}486
\end{array}
$$

a. Kiki made a mistake. What mistake did Kiki make?

_____

_____

b. Correct Kiki's mistake by multiplying 1,498 times 25. Show your work.

c. How many definitions are in the dictionary?

_____

_____

Solve. Show your work.

2. Evan spent 275 minutes each school day studying. There are 180 school days. How many minutes did Evan spend studying during the school year?

_____

_____

_____

3. There are 354 stairs in the Statue of Liberty. A tour guide has climbed the stairs in the Statue of Liberty 1,856 times. How many stairs has the tour guide climbed in the Statue of Liberty?

_____

_____

_____

4. Jada saves $175 each month. How much money has Jada saved after 24 months?

_____

_____

_____

5. A total of 4,640 people run a race. The race is 42 kilometers long. How many total kilometers are run during the race?

_____

_____

_____

Practice Dividing Using Models

Matthew used an area model to find the quotient of $1{,}236 \div 15$.
Review his work.

	80	1	
15	1,200	15	21

1. Matthew made a mistake.

   a. What was Matthew's mistake?

   _____

   _____

   _____

   b. Correct Matthew's area model in the problem.

   c. What is the correct quotient? _____ R _____

   d. What is the quotient written as a mixed number in simplest form? _____

Complete the area model to find the quotient. Write the quotient as a whole number or a mixed number in simplest form.

2. $810 \div 30 =$ _____

3. $4{,}565 \div 55 =$ _____

4. $390 \div 12 =$ _____

5. $7{,}050 \div 40 =$ _____

Multidigit Division Strategies (B)

Practice Writing Equations for Division Models

Complete the division equation using the division model.

1. This division model represents the quotient $537 \div 12$.

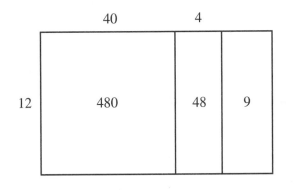

	40	4	
12	480	48	9

a. Fill in each blank with an area from the division model. Write the areas in order from left to right.

$537 \div 12 = ($ _____ $\div 12) + ($ _____ $\div 12) + ($ _____ $\div 12)$

b. Evaluate the operation in each parentheses from Part (a). Write the remainder as a fraction with 12 in the denominator.

$537 \div 12 =$ _____ $+$ _____ $+$ _____

c. Add the numbers in Part (b) to get the quotient as a mixed number in simplest form.

$537 \div 12 =$ _____

Look at that! The equations and the area model show the same thing.

Draw an area model, and then write division equations to find each quotient.

2. $572 \div 11$

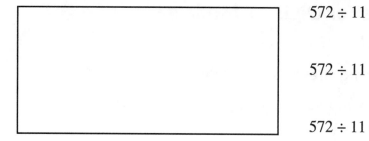

$572 \div 11 = \underline{\hspace{4cm}}$

$572 \div 11 = \underline{\hspace{4cm}}$

$572 \div 11 = \underline{\hspace{4cm}}$

3. $5{,}293 \div 67$

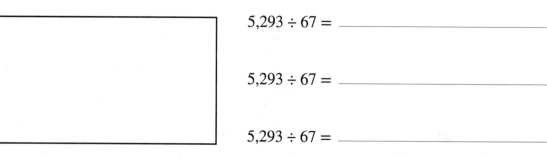

$5{,}293 \div 67 = \underline{\hspace{4cm}}$

$5{,}293 \div 67 = \underline{\hspace{4cm}}$

$5{,}293 \div 67 = \underline{\hspace{4cm}}$

4. $882 \div 21$

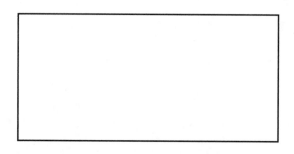

$882 \div 21 = \underline{\hspace{4cm}}$

$882 \div 21 = \underline{\hspace{4cm}}$

$882 \div 21 = \underline{\hspace{4cm}}$

5. $7{,}626 \div 31$

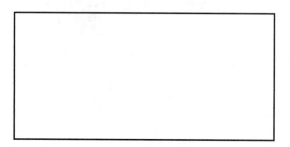

$7{,}626 \div 31 = \underline{\hspace{4cm}}$

$7{,}626 \div 31 = \underline{\hspace{4cm}}$

$7{,}626 \div 31 = \underline{\hspace{4cm}}$

Multidigit Division Algorithm (A)

Practice Dividing 2-Digit Numbers by 2-Digit Numbers

Sarah divided 90 by 15. Review her work.

$$15\overline{)90} \\ \underset{}{\overset{4}{}} \\ -60 \\ \overline{30}$$

1. Sarah's work is incorrect.

   a. What mistake did Sarah make? How do you know?

   _____

   _____

   _____

   b. What is the correct quotient of 90 and 15? Show your work.

   $$15\overline{)90}$$

Divide. Show your work. Write your answer as a whole number.

2. $23\overline{)92}$

3. $18\overline{)54}$

Divide. Show your work. Write your answer as a mixed number in simplest form.

4. 16) 94   _____

5. 12) 76   _____

Answer the questions. Show your work.

6. Jordan is preparing servings of baby carrots. He has 96 baby carrots. Each serving is 12 carrots.

    a. How many servings can Jordan prepare? _____

    b. Will Jordan have any carrots left over? Why or why not?

    _____

    _____

7. Eloise is creating 14 school-supply kits to donate. She wants to include the same number of pencils in each kit. She has 80 pencils.

    a. How many pencils will each kit contain? _____

    b. How many pencils will be left over? _____

> Working out the solution on paper is much easier than trying to keep track of everything in my head!

Multidigit Division Algorithm (B)

Practice Dividing 3-Digit Numbers by 2-Digit Numbers

Eric divided 477 by 35. Review the first step of his work.

$$
\begin{array}{r}
1 \\
35\overline{)477} \\
-35 \\
\hline
442
\end{array}
$$

1. Eric made a mistake. What mistake did Eric make?

   _____

   _____

   _____

Divide. Show your work. Write your answer as a whole number.

2. $15\overline{)795}$

3. $11\overline{)748}$

Divide. Show your work. Write your answer as a mixed number in simplest form.

4.  12) ‾‾594‾‾ _____

5. 16) ‾‾586‾‾ _____

Answer the question. Show your work.

6. Maria is constructing several birdhouses. She has only one box of nails containing 550 nails. Each birdhouse requires 21 nails.

   How many nails will be left over?

   _____

    21) ‾‾550‾‾

7. Rami's piano teacher challenged him to practice for a total of 630 minutes in one month. The month has 30 days.

   How many minutes must Rami practice each day to meet the goal?

   _____

    30) ‾‾630‾‾

Multidigit Division Algorithm (C)

Practice Dividing 4-Digit Numbers by 2-Digit Numbers

Amelie divided 9,648 by 48. Review her work.

$$
\begin{array}{r}
2\ 1 \\
48\overline{)9{,}648} \\
-9{,}600 \\
\hline
48 \\
-48 \\
\hline
0
\end{array}
$$

1. Amelie says the quotient is 21. But, she made a mistake.

   a. What mistake did Amelie make?

   _____

   _____

   _____

   b. What is the correct quotient of 9,648 and 48? _____

Divide. Show your work. Write your answer as a whole number.

2. $65\overline{)\ \ \ 1{,}625}$

3. $28\overline{)\ \ \ 5{,}852}$

Divide. Show your work. Write your answer as a whole number followed by the remainder using R.

4. 22) ‾‾‾‾7,562   □ _____

5. 61) ‾‾‾‾3,068   □ _____

Answer the question. Show your work.

6. James is writing a report. The report must have at least 1,210 words. The report is due in 11 days. He wants to split up the writing evenly on each day. How many words must James write each day to complete his report on time?

_____

□

11) ‾‾‾‾1,210

Math can be found in the stories I read and the research I do for reports.

Addition of Fractions (A)

Practice Adding Fractions with Like Denominators

Answer the questions.

1. Min is using a model to add $\frac{3}{10}$ and $\frac{4}{10}$. First, he draws a rectangle and separates it into 10 equal pieces. Then, he shades 3 of those pieces.

   a. What should Min do next?

   _____

   _____

   _____

   b. Min is confused about whether the answer should be $\frac{7}{10}$ or $\frac{7}{20}$. Which answer is correct? How do you know?

   _____

   _____

Add. Write your answer in simplest form.

2. $\begin{array}{r} \frac{9}{16} \\ + \frac{6}{16} \\ \hline \end{array}$

3. $\begin{array}{r} \frac{5}{20} \\ + \frac{12}{20} \\ \hline \end{array}$

4. $\frac{10}{25} + \frac{4}{25} =$ _____

5. $\frac{4}{12} + \frac{2}{12} =$ _____

6. $\frac{2}{18} + \frac{16}{18} =$ _____

7. $\frac{12}{45} + \frac{15}{45} =$ _____

Answer the question with a complete sentence. Show your work.

8. Evan completes $\frac{3}{12}$ of his assignment before soccer practice. He completes $\frac{8}{12}$ of his assignment after practice. How much of his assignment has Evan completed so far?

_____

_____

_____

9. Sarah runs three sprints. The first sprint is $\frac{3}{10}$ mile. The second and third sprints are each $\frac{2}{10}$ mile. How far does Sarah run altogether?

_____

_____

_____

Practice Generating Equivalent Fractions

Answer the questions.

1. Eric, Maria, and Eloise are trying to generate a fraction that is equivalent to $\frac{8}{10}$.

   a. Eric multiplies the numerator and denominator by 2.

      What is Eric's equivalent fraction? _____

   b. Maria divides the numerator and denominator by 2.

      What is Maria's equivalent fraction? _____

   c. Eloise adds 2 to the numerator and denominator to get $\frac{10}{12}$.

      Is Eloise's fraction equivalent to $\frac{8}{10}$? _____

      Draw two fractions strips to explain your answer.

      ```
      ┌─────────────────────────────────────────────┐
      │                                             │
      └─────────────────────────────────────────────┘
      ```

      ```
      ┌─────────────────────────────────────────────┐
      │                                             │
      └─────────────────────────────────────────────┘
      ```

2. What fraction is equivalent to $\frac{1}{4}$ and has a denominator of 60? _____

3. What fraction is equivalent to $\frac{18}{30}$ and has a numerator of 3? _____

Write a number in the box to create equivalent fractions.

4. $\dfrac{8}{44} = \dfrac{\boxed{}}{11}$

5. $\dfrac{2}{3} = \dfrac{18}{\boxed{}}$

6. $\dfrac{\boxed{}}{63} = \dfrac{5}{21}$

7. $\dfrac{2}{\boxed{}} = \dfrac{10}{20}$

Write three fractions that are equivalent to the given fraction.

8. $\dfrac{21}{24}$ _____ _____ _____

9. $\dfrac{30}{45}$ _____ _____ _____

Write a fraction equivalent to the given fraction by dividing by the greatest common factor.

10. $\dfrac{18}{60}$ _____

> Wow! Every fraction can be written many different ways.

Addition of Fractions (C)

Practice Writing Fractions in Different Forms

Nick and Natalie both simplify $\frac{30}{45}$. Review their work.

Nick's work: $\frac{30 \div 15}{45 \div 15} = \frac{2}{3}$

Natalie's work: $\frac{30 \div 3}{45 \div 3} = \frac{10 \div 5}{15 \div 5} = \frac{2}{3}$

1. Both students simplify correctly, but each student uses a different strategy.

   a. Which student divides by the greatest common factor of 30 and 45? _____

   b. Which student divides by two common factors of 30 and 45? _____

   c. Which strategy do you prefer?

   _____

   _____

   _____

Dividing by the greatest common factor is the greatest way to simplify fractions.

Write the fraction in simplest form.

2. $\frac{20}{25}$ _____

3. $\frac{21}{49}$ _____

4. $\frac{66}{88}$ _____

5. $\frac{27}{45}$ _____

Write the improper fraction as a mixed number in simplest form.

6. $\frac{36}{7}$ _____

7. $\frac{67}{3}$ _____

8. $\frac{66}{21}$ _____

9. $\frac{116}{40}$ _____

10. $\frac{60}{26}$ _____

11. $\frac{71}{50}$ _____

Practice Adding Fractions with Unlike Denominators

Answer the questions.

1. Jordan is working on this addition problem:

    $$\frac{8}{15} + \frac{1}{6}$$

    He decides to use 60 as a common denominator because $15 \times 4 = 60$ and $6 \times 10 = 60$.

    a. Jordan selects a common denominator but not the *least* common denominator. What is the least common denominator for this addition problem?

    _____

    b. Since Jordan is not using the least common denominator, he needs an extra step after he adds the fractions. What does Jordan need to do once he adds the fractions?

    _____

    _____

2. Kiki is working on this addition problem:

    $$\frac{9}{10} + \frac{8}{9}$$

    She thinks that $\frac{10}{11}$ is a reasonable answer to the addition problem.

    Is Kiki's answer reasonable? Explain your answer.

    _____

    _____

    _____

Add. Write your answer in simplest form.

3. $\dfrac{17}{30} + \dfrac{1}{2}$ _____

4. $\dfrac{5}{24} + \dfrac{1}{8}$ _____

5. $\dfrac{11}{18} + \dfrac{4}{9}$ _____

6. $\dfrac{13}{20} + \dfrac{5}{8}$ _____

7. $\dfrac{24}{25} + \dfrac{1}{20}$ _____

8. $\dfrac{5}{6} + \dfrac{3}{7}$ _____

9. $\dfrac{11}{18} + \dfrac{7}{12}$ _____

10. $\dfrac{4}{7} + \dfrac{16}{21}$ _____

Addition of Fractions (E)

Practice Adding Fractions in the Real World

Answer the questions.

1. Rami rides his bike $\frac{5}{6}$ mile to the store. Then, he rides $\frac{2}{3}$ mile to his friend's home.

   a. Estimate the distance Rami rides his bike.

   _____

   b. How far does Rami actually ride his bike? _____

2. Jada earns money babysitting. She spends $\frac{3}{8}$ of her money on drawing supplies and $\frac{2}{5}$ of her money on a new backpack. Jada estimates that she spends less than $\frac{1}{2}$ of the money she earns babysitting.

   a. Is Jada's estimate reasonable? Explain your answer.

   _____

   _____

   _____

   _____

   _____

   b. What fraction of her money does Jada actually spend? _____

Solve. Write your answer as a fraction or mixed number in simplest form.

3. Eloise spends $\frac{1}{4}$ hour drawing before lunch. She spends $\frac{5}{6}$ hour drawing after lunch.

   How long does Eloise spend drawing? _____

4. Amelie completes $\frac{1}{2}$ of her chores on Saturday and $\frac{2}{5}$ of her chores on Sunday.

   What fraction of her chores does Amelie complete? _____

5. Juan is completing a science experiment with two parts. He needs $\frac{5}{8}$ liter of water for the first part and $\frac{4}{5}$ liter of water for the second part.

   How much water does he need for the experiment? _____

Fractions are everywhere!

Addition of Fractions (F)

Practice Solving Multistep Problems by Adding Fractions

Jada and Natalie solve an addition problem. Each student uses a slightly different method. Review their work.

Jada's work: $\frac{1}{6} + \frac{2}{3} + \frac{3}{7} = \frac{7}{42} + \frac{28}{42} + \frac{18}{42} = \frac{7 + 28 + 18}{42} = \frac{53}{42} = 1\frac{11}{42}$

Natalie's work: $\frac{1}{6} + \frac{2}{3} + \frac{3}{7} = \frac{1}{6} + \frac{4}{6} + \frac{3}{7} = \frac{5}{6} + \frac{3}{7} = \frac{35}{42} + \frac{18}{42} = \frac{53}{42} = 1\frac{11}{42}$

1. Both students arrive at the correct answer.

   a. Which student finds the LCD for all three fractions in the first step? _____

   b. Which student finds the LCD of two fractions two different times? _____

   c. Whose method do you prefer? Explain your choice.

   _____

   _____

   _____

Add. Write your answer in simplest form.

2. $\frac{3}{4} + \frac{1}{5} + \frac{2}{3}$ _____

3. $\frac{8}{9} + \frac{1}{2} + \frac{5}{8}$ _____

4. $\frac{5}{12} + \frac{3}{4} + \frac{3}{8}$ _____

5. $\frac{2}{7} + \frac{1}{6} + \frac{1}{2}$ _____

6. $\frac{1}{3} + \frac{3}{10} + \frac{2}{3} + \frac{1}{10}$ _____

7. $\frac{5}{6} + \frac{1}{2} + \frac{1}{3} + \frac{1}{6}$ _____

Solve. Show your work to support your answer.

8. Amelie has an apple that weighs $\frac{1}{3}$ pound and a banana that weighs $\frac{1}{6}$ pound. Evan has an apple that weighs $\frac{1}{4}$ pound and a banana that weighs $\frac{3}{8}$ pound.

   Whose fruit weighs less?

   _____

   _____

   _____

   _____

9. Eric rides his bike down three different streets to get from his home to the pool. He rides $\frac{1}{8}$ mile down the first street, $\frac{1}{4}$ mile down the second street, and $\frac{5}{12}$ mile down the third street.

   How far does Eric travel to get to the pool?

   _____

   _____

Practice Subtracting Fractions with Like Denominators

Answer the questions.

1. Jessica is using a model to subtract $\frac{3}{10}$ from $\frac{3}{10}$. First, she draws a rectangle and separates it into 10 equal pieces. Then, she shades 3 of those pieces.

    a. What should Jessica do next?

    _____

    _____

    b. Jessica is confused about whether the answer should be $\frac{0}{10}$ or 0. Which answer is correct? How do you know?

    _____

    _____

    _____

Subtract. Write your answer in simplest form.

2. $\frac{6}{11}$
   $-\frac{2}{11}$
   _____

3. $\frac{21}{26}$
   $-\frac{19}{26}$
   _____

4. $\dfrac{16}{21} - \dfrac{5}{21}$ _____

5. $\dfrac{4}{18} - \dfrac{1}{18}$ _____

6. $\dfrac{5}{6} - \dfrac{3}{6}$ _____

7. $\dfrac{21}{40} - \dfrac{11}{40}$ _____

Answer the question in a complete sentence. Show your work.

8. The park is $\dfrac{13}{16}$ mile from Juan's home. He walks $\dfrac{7}{16}$ mile.

   How much farther must Juan walk to get to the park?

   _____

   _____

9. Aisha has a piece of ribbon that is $\dfrac{9}{10}$ meter long. She cuts a piece that
   is $\dfrac{3}{10}$ meter long.

   How much ribbon does Aisha have left?

   _____

   _____

Subtraction of Fractions (B)

Practice Subtracting Fractions from One

Answer the question.

1. Amelie is trying to subtract $1 - \frac{17}{20}$. She can't decide whether to

   rewrite 1 as $\frac{17}{17}$ or $\frac{20}{20}$.

   Which fraction should Amelie use? Explain your answer.

   _____

   _____

   _____

   _____

Subtract. Write your answer in simplest form.

2. $1 - \frac{25}{32}$ _____

3. $1 - \frac{9}{17}$ _____

The number 1 can be written as a fraction? Math is full of surprises.

4. $1 - \dfrac{27}{43}$ _____

5. $1 - \dfrac{16}{27}$ _____

6. $1 - \dfrac{53}{62}$ _____

7. $1 - \dfrac{35}{50}$ _____

8. $1 - \dfrac{1}{12}$ _____

9. $1 - \dfrac{20}{86}$ _____

10. $1 - \dfrac{76}{99}$ _____

11. $1 - \dfrac{8}{15}$ _____

Practice Subtracting Fractions with Unlike Denominators

Answer the questions.

1. Maria is working on the problem $\frac{13}{14} - \frac{3}{7}$. Why is $\frac{1}{2}$ a reasonable estimate? Fill in the blanks on each part to help Maria explain.

   a. $\frac{13}{14}$ is _____ out of _____ equal parts. It is close to

   _____.

   b. $\frac{3}{7}$ is _____ out of _____ equal parts. It is close to

   _____.

   c. $\frac{1}{2}$ _____ a reasonable estimate of $\frac{13}{14} - \frac{3}{7}$.

2. Nick is working on the problem $\frac{2}{3} - \frac{3}{5}$. He thinks that $\frac{6}{15}$ is a reasonable answer to the subtraction problem.

   Is Nick's estimate reasonable? Explain your answer.

   _____

   _____

   _____

   _____

   _____

Subtract. Write your answer in simplest form.

3. $\dfrac{7}{9} - \dfrac{4}{27}$ _____

4. $\dfrac{4}{5} - \dfrac{3}{7}$ _____

5. $\dfrac{1}{2} - \dfrac{4}{13}$ _____

6. $\dfrac{3}{5} - \dfrac{2}{6}$ _____

7. $\dfrac{11}{12} - \dfrac{12}{15}$ _____

8. $\dfrac{5}{8} - \dfrac{1}{6}$ _____

Practice Subtracting Fractions in the Real World

Answer the questions.

1. Eloise practices the violin for $\frac{7}{10}$ hour on Thursday. She practices for $\frac{1}{2}$ hour on Friday. So, Eloise practices longer on Thursday than she does on Friday.

   a. Estimate how much longer Eloise practices on Thursday.

   _____

   b. How much longer does Eloise actually practice on Thursday? Show your work.

   _____

2. Matthew has $\frac{2}{3}$ cup of raisins. He uses $\frac{1}{4}$ cup of raisins in a recipe. Matthew estimates that he has more than $\frac{1}{2}$ cup of raisins left.

   a. Is Matthew's estimate reasonable? Explain your answer.

   _____

   _____

   _____

   _____

   b. How much of a cup of raisins is actually left over? Show your work.

   _____

Solve. Write your answer as a fraction or mixed number in simplest form.

3. Rami is training for a triathlon. He needs to be able to swim $\frac{4}{5}$ kilometer. He can swim $\frac{1}{2}$ kilometer right now.

   How much farther does Rami need to be able to swim? _____

4. The members of a town council decide to spend $\frac{3}{20}$ of their budget on new playground equipment. They also decide to spend $\frac{1}{15}$ of the budget on road repairs.

   How much more of the budget will be spent on playground equipment?

   _____

5. Natalie and Jessica are each making a batch of trail mix. Natalie's recipe creates $\frac{15}{16}$ pound of trail mix. Jessica's recipe creates $\frac{3}{4}$ pound of trail mix.

   How much more trail mix does Natalie create? _____

Practice Solving Multistep Fraction Problems

Use the table to answer the questions.

1. Maria, Evan, and Eric each read before dinner and after dinner. Their reading times are recorded in the table.

	Time Before Dinner (h)	Time After Dinner (h)	Total Reading Time (h)
Maria	$\frac{1}{6}$	$\frac{3}{4}$	
Evan	$\frac{1}{2}$	$\frac{3}{8}$	
Eric	$\frac{7}{10}$	$\frac{1}{4}$	

a. How long does each person read? Complete the Total Reading Time column in the table.

b. List the readers in order of who reads for the longest time to who reads for the shortest time.

_____, _____, _____

c. Compare the two longest reading times. How much more is the longest reading time?

_____

_____

d. Compare the two shortest reading times. How much less is the shortest reading time?

_____

_____

Solve. Write your answer in simplest form.

2. $\dfrac{6}{7} - \dfrac{1}{2} - \dfrac{1}{4}$ _____

3. $\dfrac{1}{4} + \dfrac{3}{5} - \dfrac{7}{20}$ _____

4. $\dfrac{7}{12} + \left(\dfrac{5}{6} - \dfrac{1}{4} \right)$ _____

5. $\dfrac{2}{9} - \left(\dfrac{3}{4} - \dfrac{2}{3} \right)$ _____

I have to remember the order of operations with fraction problems, too!

6. $\left(\dfrac{1}{2} + \dfrac{1}{5} \right) - \left(\dfrac{3}{8} + \dfrac{1}{4} \right)$ _____

Addition of Mixed Numbers (A)

Practice Adding Mixed Numbers with Like Denominators

Answer the questions to find the sum.

1. What is $3\frac{7}{10} + 2\frac{8}{10} + 5\frac{1}{10}$?

   a. What is the sum of the whole numbers? _____

   b. What is the sum of the fractions as an improper fraction? _____

   c. What is the sum of the fractions as a mixed number in simplest form? _____

   d. What is the sum of $3\frac{7}{10} + 2\frac{8}{10} + 5\frac{1}{10}$?
      Combine the sum of the whole numbers with the sum of the

      fractions as a mixed number in simplest form. _____

Add. Write your answer as a mixed number in simplest form.

2. $5\frac{4}{7}$
   $+3\frac{2}{7}$
   _____

3. $6\frac{3}{11}$
   $+\frac{6}{11}$
   _____

4. $1\frac{6}{18} + 9\frac{3}{18} =$ _____

5. $5\frac{11}{16} + \frac{8}{16} =$ _____

> I can add whole numbers, and I can add fractions. So, I can add mixed numbers, too!

6. $15\frac{3}{6} + 2\frac{4}{6} =$ _____

7. $4\frac{13}{20} + \frac{15}{20} =$ _____

8. $3\frac{5}{14} + 1\frac{8}{14} + \frac{9}{14} =$ _____

Practice Adding Mixed Numbers with Unlike Denominators

Answer the questions to find the sum.

1. What is $1\frac{2}{5} + 1\frac{3}{10}$?

   a. Shade the boxes to represent $1\frac{2}{5}$.

   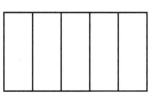

   b. Shade the boxes to represent $1\frac{3}{10}$.

   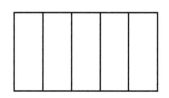

   c. The fractions do not have like denominators. How can you change the model for $1\frac{2}{5}$ to represent tenths instead of fifths?

   _____

   _____

   _____

   d. How many tenths is $\frac{2}{5}$? _____

   e. What is the sum of $1\frac{2}{5} + 1\frac{3}{10}$? Use the models to write the sum as a

   mixed number in simplest form. _____

Add. Write your answer as a mixed number in simplest form.

2. $4\frac{2}{3}$
   $+\,8\frac{1}{6}$
   _____

3. $3\frac{1}{15}$
   $+\,\frac{2}{5}$
   _____

4. $6\frac{1}{2}+3\frac{11}{13}=$ _____

5. $5\frac{1}{3}+9\frac{6}{7}=$ _____

6. $1\frac{5}{6}+8\frac{1}{4}=$ _____

7. $4\frac{5}{8}+\frac{4}{5}=$ _____

8. $7\frac{3}{5}+\frac{1}{2}+10\frac{2}{3}=$ _____

Practice Adding Mixed Numbers in the Real World

Natalie makes a mistake when she adds two mixed numbers to solve a problem. Review the problem and answer the questions.

1. Natalie programs the wheels of a robot to turn $2\frac{1}{2}$ times to reach a target. The robot misses the target. Natalie determines that the wheels need to turn another $1\frac{3}{4}$ times. When she adds $2\frac{1}{2}$ and $1\frac{3}{4}$, she gets $3\frac{5}{4}$ turns. Natalie gets an error message when she enters $3\frac{5}{4}$ turns.

   a. Does Natalie correctly add the whole number parts of the mixed numbers? Explain your answer.

   _____

   _____

   b. Does Natalie correctly add the fraction parts of the mixed numbers? Explain your answer.

   _____

   _____

   c. Why could Natalie be getting an error message?

   _____

   _____

   _____

   _____

   d. Write the number of turns as a mixed number in simplest form. _____

Solve. Write your answer as a mixed number in simplest form.

2. A plant grows $1\frac{1}{8}$ inches in a week. The plant grows $\frac{3}{4}$ inch the following week.

   How many inches does the plant grow during the 2 weeks?

   _____

3. A watermelon weighs $6\frac{13}{16}$ pounds. Another watermelon weighs

   $10\frac{1}{8}$ pounds.

   How much do the melons weigh altogether? _____

4. A recipe for bubbles requires $5\frac{1}{2}$ cups of water and $1\frac{2}{3}$ cups dish soap.

   How many cups of bubble solution does the recipe make? _____

5. Matthew is training for a race. He runs $2\frac{7}{10}$ kilometers on Saturday and $3\frac{1}{2}$ kilometers on Sunday.

   How far does Matthew run altogether? _____

Subtraction of Mixed Numbers (A)

Practice Subtracting Mixed Numbers with Like Denominators

One of these expressions has a number that must be renamed to subtract.

1. $8\frac{2}{3} - \frac{1}{3}$ $10\frac{11}{15} - 5\frac{4}{15}$ $2\frac{10}{11} - \frac{9}{11}$ $4\frac{2}{7} - 1\frac{5}{7}$

   a. Circle the expression with a number that must be renamed to subtract. Explain your choice.

   _____

   _____

   _____

   b. Subtract to find the difference of the expression you circled. Show your work, and write your answer as a mixed number in simplest form.

   _____

   _____

Subtract. Write your answer as a fraction or a mixed number in simplest form.

2. $\begin{array}{r} 7\frac{5}{6} \\ -2\frac{1}{6} \\ \hline \end{array}$

3. $\begin{array}{r} 8\frac{9}{10} \\ -\ \frac{7}{10} \\ \hline \end{array}$

4. $5\frac{1}{4} - 1\frac{3}{4} =$ _____

5. $2\frac{3}{16} - \frac{9}{16} =$ _____

6. $9\frac{4}{9} - 5\frac{7}{9} =$ _____

Knowing how to rename a mixed number can be handy in subtraction problems.

7. $1\frac{2}{13} - \frac{7}{13} =$ _____

Subtraction of Mixed Numbers (B)

Practice Subtracting Mixed Numbers with Unlike Denominators

Follow the steps to find the difference $2\frac{1}{3} - 1\frac{5}{7}$.

1. This model shows $2\frac{1}{3}$.

   a. The LCD of $\frac{1}{3}$ and $\frac{5}{7}$ is 21. Draw 6 horizontal lines to split the last box into 7 rows.

   b. Use the model to check that $\frac{1}{3} = \frac{7}{21}$ and $\frac{5}{7} = \frac{15}{21}$. There are not enough pieces to subtract these two fractions. What should you do?

   _____

   _____

   c. Draw 2 vertical lines and 6 horizontal lines to split the middle box into 21 equal pieces.

   d. Cross out 1 whole and $\frac{15}{21}$.

   _____

   _____

   e. What is $2\frac{1}{3} - 1\frac{5}{7}$? Use the models to write the difference as a

   fraction in simplest form. _____

Subtract. Write your answer as a mixed number in simplest form.

2. $12\frac{3}{4}$
   $- 4\frac{2}{3}$
   _____

3. $5\frac{7}{16}$
   $- \frac{1}{4}$
   _____

4. $11\frac{7}{9} - 9\frac{2}{3} =$ _____

5. $4\frac{1}{2} - \frac{6}{7} =$ _____

6. $12\frac{1}{3} - 3\frac{7}{10} =$ _____

7. $6\frac{2}{5} - \frac{3}{4} =$ _____

Subtraction of Mixed Numbers (C)

Practice Subtracting Mixed Numbers in the Real World

Follow the steps to solve the problem.

1. Matthew is 5 feet tall. Natalie is $3\frac{11}{12}$ feet tall.

    How much taller is Matthew than Natalie?

    a. Subtract the numbers in the correct order. _____

    b. Rename 5. _____

    c. Subtract the whole number and fraction parts. _____

    d. Answer the question with a complete sentence.

    _____

    _____

Solve. Write your answer as a mixed number in simplest form.

2. A city has $10\frac{1}{8}$ acres of land to use for a park and a nature reserve.
    The nature reserve will be $2\frac{1}{4}$ acres.

    How many acres will the park be? _____

3. Maria fills her water bottle with 32 ounces of water. Later, she notices
    that there are $5\frac{1}{4}$ ounces left in the bottle.

    How much water does Maria drink? _____

4. A farmer has $73\frac{1}{2}$ yards of fencing. He uses $70\frac{2}{3}$ yards of fencing to enclose a pasture.

   How many yards of fencing does the farmer have left over? _____

5. Juan runs a mile in $8\frac{3}{4}$ minutes. After a month of training, he can run a mile in $6\frac{7}{10}$ minutes.

   By how many minutes does Juan's time improve? _____

Subtracting mixed numbers may even help with gardening!

Practice Evaluating Multistep Expressions with Mixed Numbers

Nick evaluates the expression $9\frac{7}{11} - \left(5 + 1\frac{1}{2}\right)$. Review his work.

$$9\frac{7}{11} - \left(5 + 1\frac{1}{2}\right) = 4\frac{7}{11} + 1\frac{1}{2}$$
$$= 4\frac{14}{22} + 1\frac{11}{22}$$
$$= 5\frac{25}{22}$$
$$= 6\frac{3}{22}$$

1. Nick makes a mistake.

   a. What mistake does Nick make?

   _____

   _____

   b. What should Nick do instead?

   _____

   _____

   c. Evaluate the expression. Show your work.

   _____

   _____

Find the value of the expression. Write your answer as a mixed number or fraction in simplest form.

2. $11\frac{1}{3} + 10\frac{5}{9} - 7\frac{10}{27} =$ _____

3. $15\frac{3}{4} - 9\frac{2}{5} + 2\frac{3}{10} =$ _____

4. $4\frac{5}{8} + \left(10\frac{7}{10} - 3\frac{2}{5}\right) =$ _____

5. $2\frac{1}{6} - \left(1\frac{1}{2} - \frac{7}{9}\right) =$ _____

6. $\left(11\frac{1}{3} - 2\frac{1}{5}\right) - \left(8\frac{4}{5} - 6\frac{16}{25}\right) =$ _____

Addition and Subtraction of Mixed Numbers (B)

Practice Solving Multistep Problems with Mixed Numbers

Answer each question about the popcorn snack recipes. Write your answer in simplest form.

1. Eric and Juan each have a recipe for a popcorn snack.

Eric's Popcorn Snack	Juan's Popcorn Snack
$8\frac{1}{2}$ cups popped popcorn	$9\frac{2}{3}$ cups popped popcorn
$1\frac{2}{3}$ cups dried apples	$\frac{5}{8}$ cup raisins
$2\frac{3}{4}$ cups pine nuts	$1\frac{5}{12}$ cups toasted walnuts

a. What is the difference in each type of ingredient in the recipes? Fill in the blanks.

Popcorn: _____ needs _____ more cups than _____.

Fruit: _____ needs _____ more cups than _____.

Nuts: _____ needs _____ more cups than _____.

b. How much popcorn snack will each recipe make?

Eric's popcorn snack: _____ cups

Juan's popcorn snack: _____ cups

c. How much more popcorn snack will Eric's recipe make? _____

Solve. Write your answer in simplest form.

2. Jada bikes $4\frac{1}{2}$ kilometers and then stops to rest. After resting, Jada bikes another $1\frac{4}{5}$ kilometers. Maria bikes $7\frac{9}{10}$ kilometers without resting.

   a. How far does Jada bike altogether? _____

   b. How much farther does Maria bike than Jada? _____

3. Kiki is roping off a garden in the shape of a rectangle. Her garden measures $8\frac{3}{4}$ yards by $5\frac{7}{8}$ yards.

   a. How much rope does Kiki need to go completely around her garden? _____

   b. Kiki buys a rope that it is 35 yards long. How much rope will she have left? _____

Fractions and mixed numbers are everywhere!

Multiplying with Fractions (A)

Practice Describing Division Problems

Answer the questions.

1. Amelie has 6 feet of rope. She needs to cut it into 9 equal pieces.
    She is trying to figure out how long each piece of rope will be.

    a. Draw a model to represent the situation.

    b. Fill in the blanks to write a multiplication equation to model
        the situation.

        _____ pieces × _____ foot per piece = _____ feet total

    c. How long is each piece of rope? Write your answer as a fraction in

        simplest form. _____

Solve. Draw a model to show your work.

2. Eric has a bag of carrots that weighs 3 pounds. He separates the carrots equally into 10 containers.

   How many pounds of carrots are in each container? _____

3. Four friends must give a 7-minute presentation. Each friend must speak for an equal amount of time.

   How long will each friend speak? _____

Solve. Write a multiplication equation to show your work.

4. Three friends share 8 cups of juice. How much juice does each friend get?

   _____

5. Jessica makes 6 aprons using 5 yards of fabric. How much fabric does she use for each apron?

   _____

Practice Using a Model to Multiply a Fraction Times a Whole

Complete the models. Answer the questions.

1. Jessica is trying to find the product of 2 and $\frac{3}{5}$.

   a. Use the circles to model the product.

   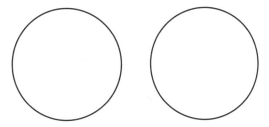

   b. Use the number line to model the product.

   0

   c. Draw an area model to represent the product.

   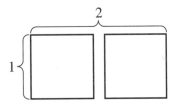

   d. Write a multiplication equation to represent the product. Write your answer in simplest form.

   _____ × _____ = _____

   e. Compare the product to the factor 2. Is the product greater than 2 or less than 2? Why?

   _____

   _____

Use the number line to solve the problem. Write your answer in simplest form.

2. $\frac{5}{9} \times 4 =$ _____

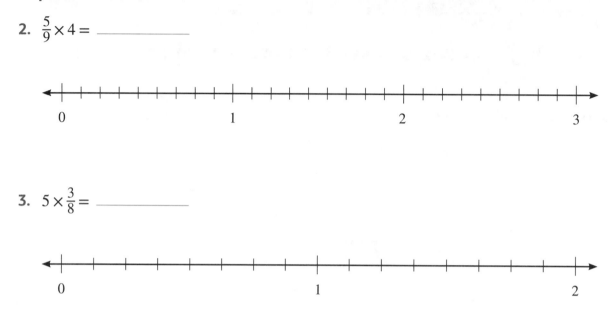

3. $5 \times \frac{3}{8} =$ _____

Draw an area model to solve the problem. Write your answer in simplest form.

4. $3 \times \frac{5}{6} =$ _____

5. $\frac{1}{4} \times 6 =$ _____

Multiplying with Fractions (C)

Practice Multiplying Whole Numbers by Fractions

Eloise writes a real-world problem to represent the product of 10 and $\frac{3}{16}$. Review her problem, and answer the questions.

> A cat weighs 10 pounds.
>
> A second cat weighs $\frac{3}{16}$ pound more.
>
> How much more does the second cat weigh?

1. Eloise's problem does **not** represent the product correctly.

   a. What mistake does Eloise make?

   _____

   _____

   _____

   b. Rewrite Eloise's problem to represent the product of 10 and $\frac{3}{16}$ correctly.

   _____

   _____

   _____

   c. Solve the problem you wrote.

   _____

   _____

Multiply. Write your answer as a fraction or a mixed number in simplest form.

2. $\frac{7}{9} \times 2 =$ _____

3. $6 \times \frac{2}{5} =$ _____

4. $8 \times \frac{11}{20} =$ _____

5. $\frac{1}{4} \times 14 =$ _____

Write a real-world problem to represent the product. Then, solve the problem.

6. $18 \times \frac{1}{4}$

Problem: _____

_____

_____

Solution: _____

7. $\frac{2}{3} \times 7$

Problem: _____

_____

_____

Solution: _____

Multiplying with Fractions (D)

Practice Multiplying Two Fractions and Determining Area

A flower bed is in the shape of a rectangle. It measures $\frac{2}{3}$ yard by $\frac{7}{8}$ yard. Find the area of the garden.

1. This square represents an area that is 1 yard by 1 yard.

    a. Show $\frac{2}{3}$ yard along one side. Divide one side into 3 equal parts and shade 2 of them.

    b. Show $\frac{7}{8}$ yard along the other side. Divide the other side into 8 equal pieces and shade 7 of them. Use a different color or pattern than the previous shading.

    c. Erase the shading on the parts that do not overlap.

    d. What is the area of the flower bed? Give your answer as a fraction in simplest form. _____

1 yd

1 yd

Write an equation that is represented by the model.

2. _____ × _____ = _____

3. _____ × _____ = _____

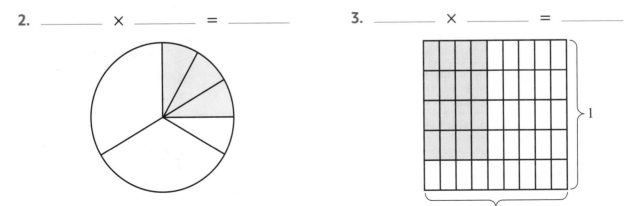

Draw a model to represent the product. Then, find the product. Write your answer as a fraction in simplest form.

4. $\frac{3}{4} \times \frac{4}{5} =$ _____

5. $\frac{1}{3} \times \frac{9}{10} =$ _____

6. $\frac{5}{6}$ cm $\times \frac{1}{4}$ cm = _____

7. $\frac{2}{7}$ mi $\times \frac{3}{8}$ mi = _____

Draw a model to solve the problem. Write your answer as a fraction in simplest form.

8. A TV screen measures $\frac{9}{10}$ meter wide and $\frac{3}{5}$ meter long.

    What is the area of the screen? _____

I can use models to understand how to multiply fractions.

Multiplying with Fractions (E)

Practice Multiplying Fractions

Answer the questions.

1. A city park is in the shape of a rectangle. One side of the park is $\frac{7}{9}$ mile and the other side is $\frac{4}{5}$ mile.

   a. What is the area of the park?

      Multiply the fractions to determine the area. _____

   b. Shade the model to show the area of the park.

      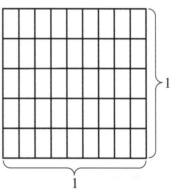

   c. How does the area found by multiplying fractions relate to the model?

      _____

      _____

      _____

      _____

      _____

      _____

Determine the fraction that completes the equation. Write your answer as a fraction in simplest form.

2. $\frac{2}{5} \times \frac{4}{7} = \frac{\boxed{}}{\boxed{}}$

3. $\frac{6}{11} \times \frac{5}{9} \times \frac{1}{4} = \frac{\boxed{}}{\boxed{}}$

4. $\frac{3}{10} \times \frac{\boxed{}}{\boxed{}} = \frac{9}{80}$

5. $\frac{\boxed{}}{\boxed{}} \times \frac{3}{4} = \frac{15}{28}$

Write a real-world problem to represent the product. Then, solve the problem.

6. $\frac{2}{5} \times \frac{1}{8}$

   Problem: _____

   _____

   _____

   Solution: _____

7. $\frac{11}{12} \times \frac{1}{3}$

   Problem: _____

   _____

   _____

   Solution: _____

Multiplying with Mixed Numbers (A)

Practice Multiplying with Mixed Numbers

Follow the instructions to complete the model. Use the model to solve the problem.

1. Jessica finishes her book in $2\frac{1}{3}$ hours. Eric takes $1\frac{1}{2}$ times longer than Jessica to finish his book.

    This model represents the amount of time Jessica takes to finish her book. It has a width of 1 and a length of $2\frac{1}{3}$.

    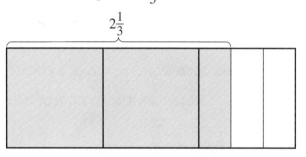

    a. Draw another row just like the first row.

    b. Divide the new row into 2 equal rows. Shade the first 3 columns of the top row.

    c. Label the width $1\frac{1}{2}$.

    d. Find the area of the shaded region by adding the parts. Fill in the boxes to find area of the shaded region.

    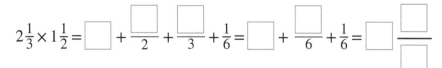

    e. How long does it take Eric to finish his book? _____

Use the model to solve the problem.

2. James is building a cabinet that will be $4\frac{1}{2}$ feet tall. The handle needs to be $\frac{5}{6}$ of the way up from the bottom of the cabinet. He draws this model to determine the height of the handle.

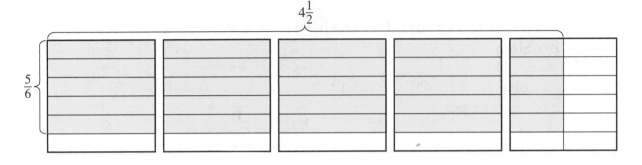

At what height should James place the handle? _____

3. A recipe calls for $3\frac{1}{4}$ cups of milk. Jada wants to make $2\frac{1}{2}$ batches of the recipe. She draws this model to determine the amount of milk needed.

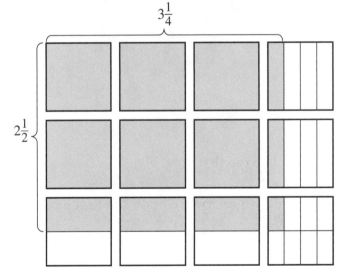

How much milk does Jada need to make $2\frac{1}{2}$ batches of the recipe? _____

Multiplying with Mixed Numbers (B)

Practice Multiplying Mixed Numbers

Follow the steps to find the product.

1. $3\frac{1}{3} \times 5\frac{3}{4} \times \frac{1}{2}$

   a. Rewrite each mixed number as an improper fraction.

   _____ × _____ × $\frac{1}{2}$

   b. Multiply the numerators, and then multiply the denominators.

   _____

   c. Rewrite the product as a mixed number in simplest form.

   _____

Find the product. Write your answer as a mixed number in simplest form.

2. $7\frac{1}{4} \times 1\frac{3}{5} =$ _____

3. $\frac{3}{8} \times 5\frac{1}{2} =$ _____

4. $2\frac{1}{7} \times 4\frac{2}{3} =$ _____

5. $6\frac{1}{2} \times 1\frac{2}{5} =$ _____

6. $3\frac{5}{8} \times \frac{5}{6} =$ _____

7. $\frac{4}{9} \times 8\frac{1}{2} =$ _____

Those fractions may be improper, but they sure help when I am multiplying a mixed number.

Multiplying with Mixed Numbers (C)

Practice Multiplying with Mixed Numbers in the Real World

This recipe is for a pitcher of lemonade. Aisha wants to make $3\frac{1}{2}$ pitchers for a party.

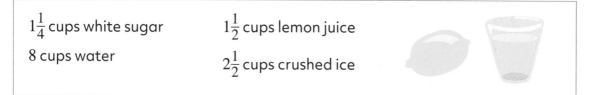

$1\frac{1}{4}$ cups white sugar

8 cups water

$1\frac{1}{2}$ cups lemon juice

$2\frac{1}{2}$ cups crushed ice

1. Calculate how much of each ingredient Aisha needs to make $3\frac{1}{2}$ pitchers of lemonade. Show your work for each step. Write your answer as a complete sentence.

   a. How much sugar does Aisha need?

   _____

   _____

   b. How much water does Aisha need?

   _____

   _____

   c. How much lemon juice does Aisha need?

   _____

   _____

   d. How much crushed ice does Aisha need?

   _____

Solve. Write your answer as a complete sentence.

2. Jordan is building a kitchen table. He wants to put glass inserts, or pieces, in the middle. The table will be $2\frac{1}{4}$ yards in length. The length of the inserts will be $\frac{2}{3}$ the length of the table.

   How long will the inserts be?

   _____

   _____

3. Sarah has a trip that is scheduled to take $1\frac{1}{5}$ hours. She has covered $\frac{5}{8}$ of the distance of her trip.
   How long has Sarah been traveling so far?

   _____

   _____

4. A railing is around a tree house. Pieces of wood that are $4\frac{2}{3}$ feet long are used to build the railing. A total of $5\frac{1}{4}$ pieces of wood are used.
   How long is the railing?

   _____

   _____

5. Eloise is $4\frac{1}{2}$ years old. Kiki is $1\frac{1}{3}$ times older than Eloise. Jada is $1\frac{1}{4}$ times older than Kiki.
   How old is Jada?

   _____

   _____

Unit Fractions Divided by Whole Numbers (A)

Practice Dividing Unit Fractions Using Models

Three students are using models to determine the quotient $\frac{1}{3} \div 4$.

Follow the instructions to complete each model. Fill in the blanks to determine the quotient.

1. Amelie is using an area model. She divides a square into 3 equal parts.

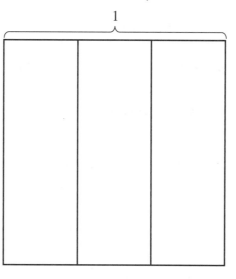

a. Shade one part to represent $\frac{1}{3}$.

b. Draw 3 horizontal lines in the shaded region to divide $\frac{1}{3}$ into 4 equal parts.

c. Erase the shading in all but one smaller square.

d. Extend each horizontal line to divide the other thirds.

e. Fill in the blanks: There are _____ rows and _____ columns,

    making a total of _____ parts. Each part is _____ of the whole.

2. Kiki is using a number line. She draws 2 tick marks that divide 1 into 3 equal parts.

0   1

a. Label the tick marks $\frac{1}{3}$ and $\frac{2}{3}$.

b. Add 3 tick marks between 0 and $\frac{1}{3}$.

c. Repeat the tick marks in the other thirds.

d. Place a point at the first tick mark.

e. Fill in the blanks: There are _____ equally spaced parts

between 0 and 1. Each tick mark represents _____ of the whole.

3. Eric is using fraction strips. He divides a rectangle into 3 equal parts.

1

a. Draw 3 vertical lines to divide $\frac{1}{3}$ into 4 equal parts.

b. Shade one new column.

c. Repeat the vertical lines in each third.

d. Fill in the blanks: One whole is divided into _____ thirds.

Each third contains _____ equal fraction pieces, making

a total of _____ parts. Each part is _____ of the whole.

Use the model to find the quotient.

4. $\frac{1}{6} \div 3 =$ _____

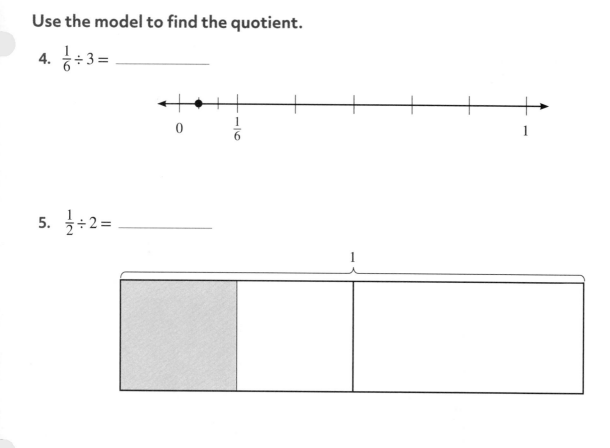

5. $\frac{1}{2} \div 2 =$ _____

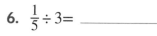

6. $\frac{1}{5} \div 3 =$ _____

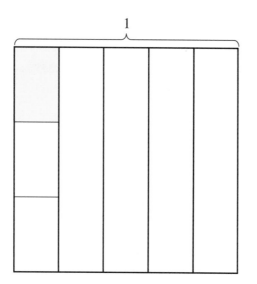

7. $\frac{1}{3} \div 2 =$ _____

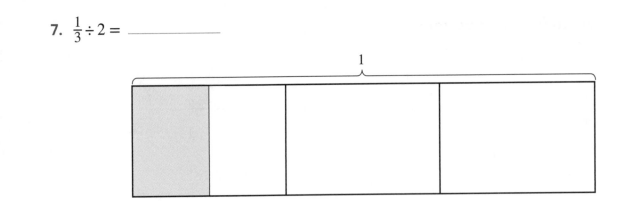

8. $\frac{1}{4} \div 3 =$ _____

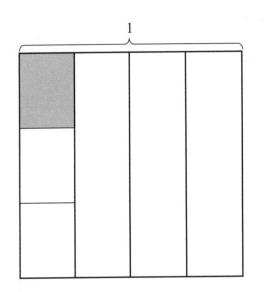

9. $\frac{1}{2} \div 4 =$ _____

Unit Fractions Divided by Whole Numbers (B)

Practice Dividing Unit Fractions with Stories

Rami writes a real-world problem to represent the quotient $\frac{1}{2} \div 3$.
Review his problem.

> A scientist has 3 containers. He pours $\frac{1}{2}$ liter of water into each container. How much water does the scientist use?

1. Rami's problem does **not** represent the quotient correctly.

   a. What mistake does Rami make?

   _____

   _____

   b. Rewrite Rami's problem to represent the quotient correctly.

   _____

   _____

   _____

   c. Use this fraction strip model to solve the problem you wrote.
      Write your answer in a complete sentence.

   1

   _____

Use the model to solve the problem. Write your answer in a complete sentence.

2. Jessica decides to spend $\frac{1}{5}$ of her allowance on 2 softballs.

   What fraction of her allowance does Jessica spend on each softball?

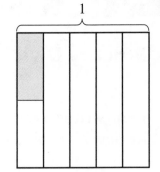

_____

_____

3. Maria purchases a bag of pet food to last 1 week, which is 7 days. Each day, she will split the portion equally between her 2 dogs.

   What fraction of the bag of food will each dog eat each day?

_____

_____

4. A relay race is $\frac{1}{2}$ mile long. There are 6 members on a relay race team. Each person will run the same distance.

   How far will each person run during the race?

_____

_____

Unit Fractions Divided by Whole Numbers (C)

Practice Dividing Unit Fractions Using Multiplication

Follow the steps to find the quotient of $\frac{1}{3}$ and 5.

1. Use the inverse relationship between multiplication and division to fill in the blanks.

   a. Fill in the blanks to write a related multiplication problem.

   $\frac{1}{3} \div 5 = ?$ because $? \times$ _____ = _____ .

   b. Rewrite the fraction as an equivalent fraction with a numerator of 5.

   $\frac{1}{3} =$ _____

   c. What is the missing factor? _____

   d. What is $\frac{1}{3} \div 5$?

   $\frac{1}{3} \div 5 =$ _____

Fill in the blanks to complete each statement and find the quotient.

2. $\frac{1}{9} \div 3 =$ _____ because _____ $\times 3 = \frac{1}{9}$.

3. $\frac{1}{7} \div 8 =$ _____ because _____ $\times$ _____ $= \frac{1}{7}$.

4. $\frac{1}{2} \div 10 =$ _____ because _____ $\times$ _____ $=$ _____ .

Determine the quotient. Explain your answer using the relationship between multiplication and division.

5. $\frac{1}{6} \div 5 = $ _____

Reason: _____

_____

6. $\frac{1}{5} \div 2 = $ _____

Reason: _____

_____

7. $\frac{1}{4} \div 7 = $ _____

Reason: _____

_____

It sure is helpful to know that multiplication and division are related.

Unit Fractions Divided by Whole Numbers (D)

Practice Dividing Unit Fractions by Using the Rule

Nick determines that the quotient of $\frac{1}{8}$ and 4 is 32. Review his work.

$$\frac{1}{8} \div 4 = 8 \times 4 = 32$$

1. Nick makes a mistake.

   a. What mistake does Nick make?

   _____

   _____

   b. What is the correct quotient? Show your work.

   _____

Divide. Give your answer as a fraction in simplest form.

2. $\frac{1}{10} \div 2 =$ _____

3. $\frac{1}{2} \div 4 =$ _____

4. $\frac{1}{9} \div 2 = $ _____

5. $\frac{1}{3} \div 7 = $ _____

6. $\frac{1}{5} \div 3 = $ _____

7. $\frac{1}{7} \div 4 = $ _____

8. $\frac{1}{4} \div 5 = $ _____

9. $\frac{1}{6} \div 3 = $ _____

To find the reciprocal of a whole number, write it with a denominator of 1 and then flip it!

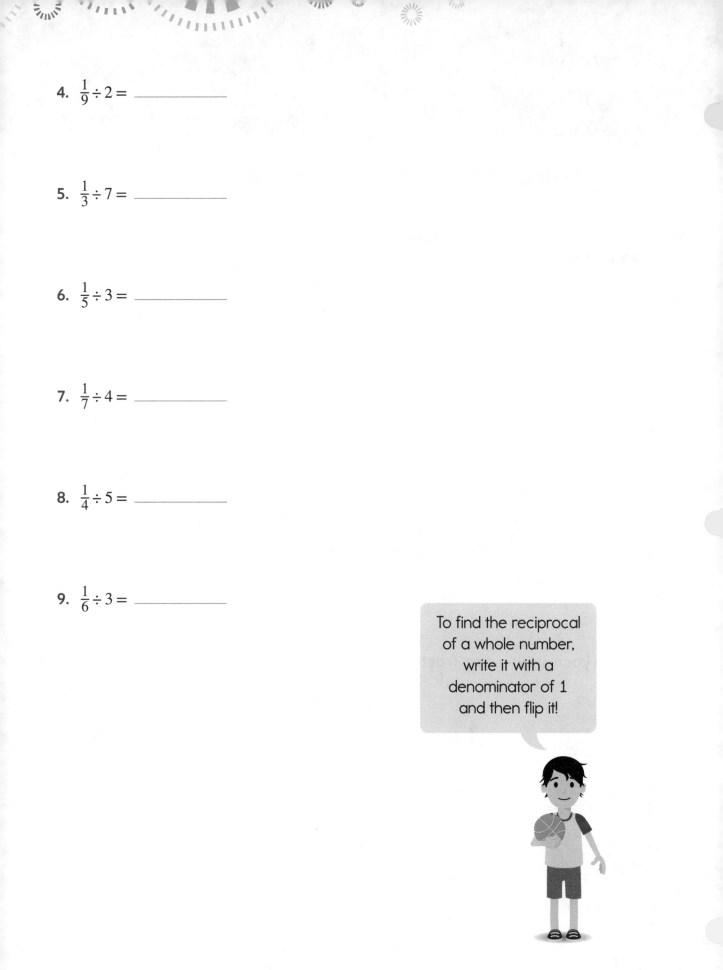

Unit Fractions Divided by Whole Numbers (E)

Practice Dividing Unit Fractions to Solve Real-World Problems

Answer the questions to solve the problem.

1. Three-quarters of a carrot cake is eaten during a party. Evan and his friend want to split the remaining cake into two equal pieces to eat.

   a. What fraction of the cake is remaining?

   _____

   _____

   b. What division problem represents this situation?

   _____

   c. How much of the cake will Evan get? Write your answer in a complete sentence.

   _____

   _____

Solve. Write your answer in a complete sentence.

2. One-third of the stamps in Amelie's stamp collection are squares. There are an equal number of square stamps that contain images of people, animals, and flags.

   What fraction of Amelie's stamp collection is square flag stamps?

   _____

   _____

   _____

3. Min has a board that is $\frac{1}{5}$ meter long. He cuts the board into 2 equal pieces.

    How long is each piece?

    _____

    _____

    _____

4. Aisha has $\frac{1}{4}$ pint of paint. She needs to paint all faces of a cube, which has 6 faces. She must use the same amount of paint on each face.

    How much paint will Aisha use on each face of the cube?

    _____

    _____

    _____

5. Jordan has $\frac{1}{2}$ hour to exercise. He wants to spend an equal amount of time stretching, doing jumping jacks, doing push-ups, doing sit-ups, and cooling down.

    How long will Jordan spend doing each part of his workout?

    _____

    _____

    _____

Whole Numbers Divided by Unit Fractions (A)

Practice Dividing by Unit Fractions Using Models

Two students are using models to determine the quotient $3 \div \frac{1}{4}$.

Follow the instructions to complete each model. Fill in the blanks to determine the quotient.

1. Maria is using an area model. She starts by drawing 3 equal squares.

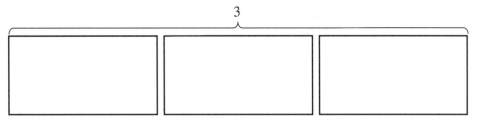

    a. Draw 3 vertical lines in each square to show dividing by $\frac{1}{4}$.

    b. Count the number of fourths in the model.

    c. Fill in the blanks: There are _____ fourths in 3, so $3 \div \frac{1}{4} =$ _____.

2. Jordan is using a number line. He draws a number line with tick marks to represent 0, 1, 2, and 3.

    a. Add 3 tick marks each between 0 and 1, 1 and 2, and 2 and 3 to divide each whole into fourths.

    b. Count the number of one-fourth jumps between 0 and 3.

    c. Fill in the blanks: There are _____ one-fourth jumps between

        0 and 3, so $3 \div \frac{1}{4} =$ _____.

Use the model to find the quotient.

3. $2 \div \frac{1}{7} =$ _____

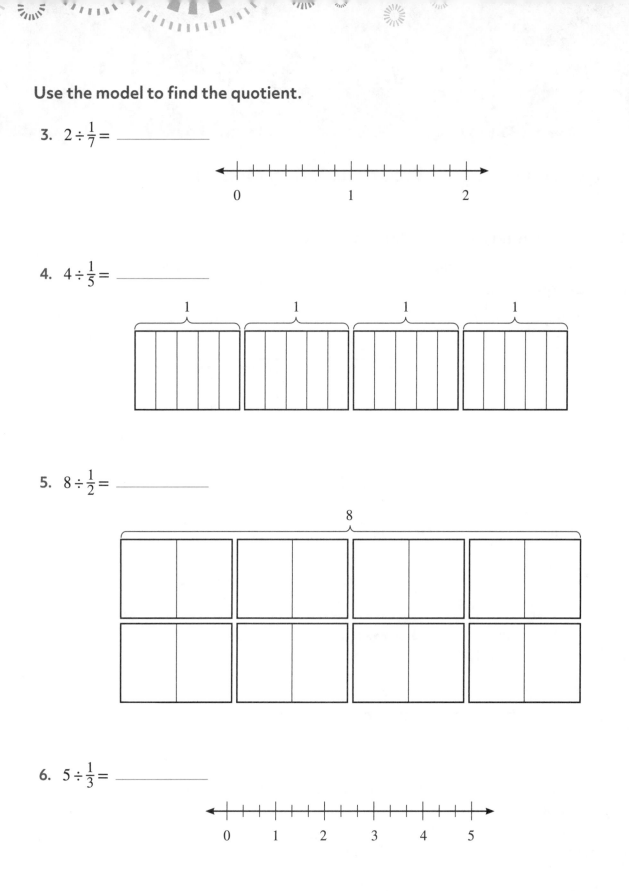

4. $4 \div \frac{1}{5} =$ _____

5. $8 \div \frac{1}{2} =$ _____

6. $5 \div \frac{1}{3} =$ _____

Whole Numbers Divided by Unit Fractions (B)

Practice Dividing by Unit Fractions with Stories

Jada writes a real-world problem to represent the quotient $9 \div \frac{1}{2}$.
Review her problem.

> I have 9 cups of blueberries in a bowl.
>
> I pour in another $\frac{1}{2}$ cup of blueberries.
>
> How many cups of blueberries do I have?

1. Jada's problem does **not** represent the quotient correctly.

   a. What mistake does Jada make?

   _____

   _____

   b. Rewrite Jada's problem to represent the quotient correctly.

   _____

   _____

   _____

   _____

   c. Use this model to solve the problem you wrote.

   _____

Write a real-world problem to describe the expression.

2. $6 \div \frac{1}{4}$

_____

_____

_____

3. $8 \div \frac{1}{3}$

_____

_____

_____

Use the model to solve the problem. Write your answer in a complete sentence.

4. Evan has 7 pounds of food for his dog. He gives his dog $\frac{1}{2}$ pound of food each day.

   How many days will Evan be able to feed his dog using the food he has?

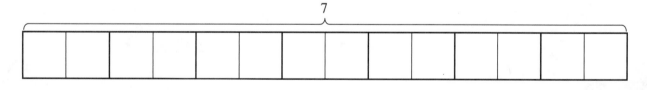

_____

5. Kiki has 4 kilograms of fertilizer for her plants. Each plant needs $\frac{1}{5}$ kilogram of fertilizer.

   How many plants will Kiki be able to fertilize?

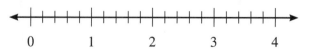

_____

Whole Numbers Divided by Unit Fractions (C)

Practice Dividing by Unit Fractions Using Multiplication

Follow the steps to find the quotient $4 \div \frac{1}{7}$.

1. Use the inverse relationship between multiplication and division to fill in the blanks.

   a. Fill in the blanks to write a related multiplication problem.

   $4 \div \frac{1}{7} = ?$ because $4 =$ _____ $\times$ _____ .

   b. The whole number is written as a fraction with a denominator of 1. Rewrite this fraction as an equivalent fraction with a denominator of 7.

   $\frac{4}{1} =$ _____

   c. What is the missing factor in the multiplication problem? _____

   d. What is $4 \div \frac{1}{7}$?

   $4 \div \frac{1}{7} =$ _____

Fill in the blanks to complete the statement and find the quotient.

2. $3 \div \frac{1}{4} =$ _____ because _____ $\times \frac{1}{4} = 3$.

3. $8 \div \frac{1}{5} =$ _____ because _____ $\times$ _____ $= 8$.

4. $7 \div \frac{1}{2} =$ _____ because _____ $\times$ _____ $=$ _____ .

Determine the quotient. Explain your answer using the relationship between multiplication and division.

5. $9 \div \frac{1}{4} = $ _____

Reason: _____

_____

6. $5 \div \frac{1}{3} = $ _____

Reason: _____

_____

7. $10 \div \frac{1}{2} = $ _____

Reason: _____

_____

> Dividing by a fraction looks tricky, but I can use a related multiplication problem to figure it out.

Whole Numbers Divided by Unit Fractions (D)

Practice Dividing by Unit Fractions Using the Rule

Aisha determines that the quotient $10 \div \frac{1}{3}$ is $\frac{3}{10}$. Review her work.

$$10 \div \frac{1}{3} = \frac{1}{10} \times \frac{3}{1} = \frac{3}{10}$$

1. Aisha makes a mistake.

   a. What mistake does Aisha make?

   _____

   _____

   _____

   b. What is the correct quotient? Show your work.

   _____

   _____

   _____

When I divide by a fraction correctly, I feel like singing!

Divide. Write your answer as a whole number.

2. $5 \div \frac{1}{10} =$ _____

3. $4 \div \frac{1}{8} =$ _____

4. $11 \div \frac{1}{2} =$ _____

5. $8 \div \frac{1}{5} =$ _____

6. $7 \div \frac{1}{9} =$ _____

7. $9 \div \frac{1}{2} =$ _____

8. $3 \div \frac{1}{7} =$ _____

9. $6 \div \frac{1}{6} =$ _____

Whole Numbers Divided by Unit Fractions (E)

Practice Dividing by Unit Fractions in the Real World

Fill in the blanks to solve the problem.

1. A batch of slime requires $\frac{1}{2}$ cup of glue and $\frac{1}{3}$ cup of laundry detergent. Sarah has 6 cups of glue and 5 cups of laundry detergent.

   What is the maximum number of batches of slime Sarah can make?

   a. Sarah has enough glue to make _____ batches of slime.

   b. Sarah has enough laundry detergent to make _____ batches of slime.

   c. Sarah can only make _____ batches of slime. She will have

   some _____ left over.

Solve. Write your answer in a complete sentence.

2. A clothing company has machines that can each produce 1 yard of fabric in $\frac{1}{6}$ hour.

   a. How many yards of fabric can a machine produce in 8 hours?

   _____

   _____

   _____

   b. How many yards of fabric can 36 machines produce in 1 hour?

   _____

   _____

3. Nick purchases some helium tanks to inflate balloons for a party. Each tank contains 9 cubic feet of helium. Each balloon will be filled with $\frac{1}{2}$ cubic foot of helium.

   a. How many balloons can each tank of helium fill?

   _____

   _____

   _____

   b. Nick needs to inflate 30 balloons. He has 2 tanks of helium.

   Will Nick have enough helium to inflate his balloons? Explain your answer.

   _____

   _____

   _____

Measuring Volume (A)

Practice Understanding and Measuring Volume

Answer the questions.

1. Determine whether each statement is True or False.

   a. A unit cube could be 6 units long by 6 units wide by 6 units tall. _____

   b. Volume can be measured by packing a solid with unit cubes

   as long as there are no gaps or overlaps. _____

2. Match the definition on the left to the correct term on the right.

the distance around the edge of a shape ○	○	volume
the amount of space on a flat surface ○	○	perimeter
the amount of space taken up by a three-dimensional object ○	○	area

Volume tells me how much space is inside a three-dimensional object.

Sarah measures the volume of this rectangular prism.

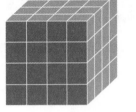

3. Sarah counts 7 cubes in each of the bottom three rows and 16 cubes in the top row. She determines that the volume of the cube is $7 + 7 + 7 + 16 = 37$ units^3.

   a. The volume Sarah finds is **not** correct. What mistake does Sarah make?

   _____

   _____

   _____

   _____

   b. What is the correct volume of the rectangular prism?
      Show your work.

   _____

Find the volume of the figure.

4. volume = _____

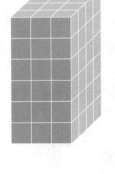

5. volume = _____

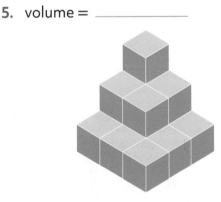

Practice Measuring Volume with Various Cubic Units

Answer the questions.

1. Circle each unit cube. (Hint: There are two unit cubes.)

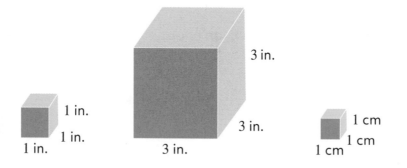

2. Jada is filling a box with 1-inch cubes. She fills the bottom layer with 1 layer of cubes. Jada wants to completely fill the box.

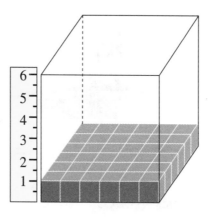

a. How many cubes are already in the box? _____ cubes

b. How many layers of cubes can Jada fit in the box? _____ layers

c. How many cubes will Jada use in all? _____ cubes

d. What is the volume of the box? _____ in^3

3. Evan is unpacking a container that is completely packed with boxes of crayons.

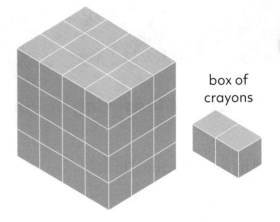

box of crayons

a. How many boxes of crayons are

in the top layer? _____ boxes

b. How many layers of crayon boxes are

in the box? _____ layers

c. How many boxes of crayons will Evan unpack? _____ boxes

Solve.

4. There are 15 cubes in each layer of this rectangular prism.

Each cube is 1 cm^3. What is the volume of this prism? _____

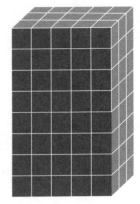

5. Each cube in this solid is 1 ft^3.

What is the volume of this solid?

_____

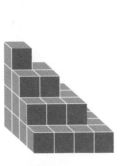

6. A food company is boxing up chicken pot pies to send to stores.

How many pot pies will fit into the shipping box? _____

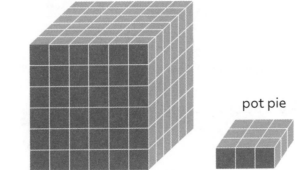

pot pie

Practice Representing Volume Using Products

Answer the questions.

1. This rectangular prism is made of unit cubes.

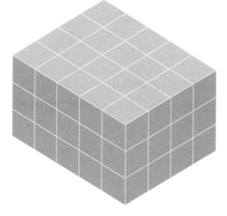

a. What are the dimensions of this rectangular prism?

length = _____

width = _____

height = _____

area of the base = _____

b. Write an expression to represent the volume of this prism using the length, the width, and the height.

volume = _____ × _____ × _____

c. Write an expression to represent the volume of this prism using the area of the base and the height.

volume = _____ × _____

d. What is the volume of the rectangular prism by counting unit cubes? _____

e. Does multiplying the length, the width, and the height give the same volume as counting unit cubes? Explain.

_____

f. Does multiplying the area of the base and the height give the same volume as counting unit cubes? Explain.

_____

Write an expression to represent the volume of the rectangular prism using the product of the length, the width, and the height.

2. volume = _____ × _____ × _____

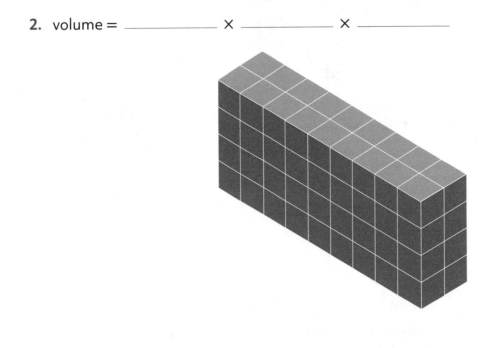

3. volume = _____ × _____ × _____

4. volume = _____ × _____ × _____

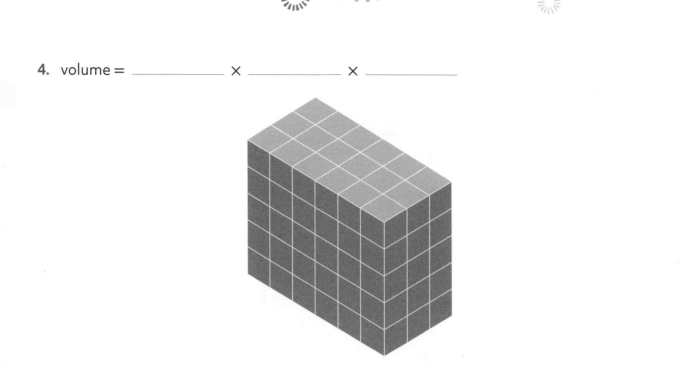

Write an expression to represent the volume of the rectangular prism using the area of the base and the height.

5. volume = _____ × _____

6. volume = _____ × _____

7. volume = _____ × _____

Calculating volume by multiplying is easy because I know my math facts!

Practice Calculating Volume Using a Formula

Answer the questions.

1. A gift box measures 6 inches long by 2 inches wide by 7 inches tall.

   a. What are the dimensions of the box?

   $l =$ _____

   $w =$ _____

   $h =$ _____

   $B =$ _____

   b. Write an expression to represent the volume of the box using the length, the width, and the height.

   $V = l \times w \times h =$ _____ $\times$ _____ $\times$ _____

   c. Write an expression to represent the volume of this prism using the area of the base and the height.

   $V = B \times h =$ _____ $\times$ _____

   d. What is the volume of the rectangular prism?

   $V =$ _____

Find the volume of the rectangular prism.

2.

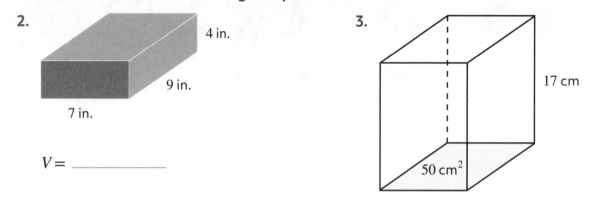

4 in.

9 in.

7 in.

$V =$ _____

3.

17 cm

50 cm^2

$V =$ _____

4. The floor of a room in the shape of a rectangular prism is covered by 30 square meters of tile. The height of the room is 3 meters.

$V =$ _____

5. A shipping box has a length of 6 feet, a width of 12 feet, and a height of 13 feet.

$V =$ _____

6.

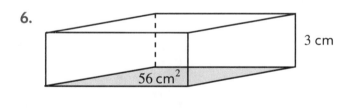

3 cm

56 cm^2

$V =$ _____

7. This cube has a side length of 5 meters.

5 m

$V =$ _____

Calculating Volume (C)

Practice Finding Missing Measurements in Volume Problems

Answer the questions.

1. The volume of this storage container is 1,400 cubic inches. The length is 20 inches and the width is 14 inches.

? in.

14 in.

20 in.

a. Which measurement is missing? _____

b. Substitute the known measurements into the formula $V = l \times w \times h$.

_____

_____

c. Which division equation will help you find the missing measurement? Circle the correct answer.

$1,400 \div h = 280$ $1,400 \div 280 = h$

d. What is the missing measurement? _____

Use the volume formula $V = l \times w \times h$ or $V = B \times h$ to solve.

2. The volume of this rectangular prism is 72 cubic meters.

What is the width of the prism? _____

2 m

? m

6 m

3. The volume of a rectangular prism is 24 cubic centimeters. The area of the base is 6 square centimeters.

   What is the height of the prism? _____

4. The volume of a rectangular prism is 50 cubic feet. The height of the prism is 2 feet.

   a. What is the area of the base of the prism? _____

   b. The base of the prism is a square. How long is each side of the square? _____

I can use formulas
to find the volume of
my present.

Practice Calculating Volume in the Real World

Follow the steps to solve the problem.

1. A cereal box is 10 inches long by 2 inches wide by 12 inches tall. The company that makes the cereal wants to increase the volume of the cereal box by 90 cubic inches. The width of the box must stay the same, but the length of the cereal box will increase by 1 inch.

    How tall should the new cereal box be?

    a. Calculate the volume of the original cereal box.

        original volume = _____

    b. Add 90 cubic inches to the original volume to find the new volume.

        new volume = _____

    c. Add 1 inch to the original length to find the length of the new box.

        new length = _____

    d. Write an equation using the formula $V = l \times w \times h$ using the new volume, the new length, the original width, and h for the new height.

        _____

    e. Circle the division equation that should be used to find the height of the new cereal box.

        $330 \div h = 22$ $330 \div 22 = h$

    f. Find the height of the new cereal box.

        new height = _____

Solve.

2. A cabinet is in the shape of a rectangular prism. The volume of the cabinet is 24 cubic feet. The base area of the cabinet is 8 square feet.

   What is the height of the cabinet? _____

3. James needs to purchase two ceiling fans. He must select the correct size of fan. The size of a ceiling fan depends on the volume of air in a room. This table shows the size of fan needed for different sizes of rooms.

Ceiling fan size	Room size (cm^3)
small	less than 48 m^3
medium	48 m^3 to 75 m^3
large	75 m^3 to 147 m^3
extra large	greater than 147 m^3

a. What size ceiling fan does James need for a room that is 6 meters by 5 meters by 3 meters? Explain your answer.

   _____

   _____

   _____

b. What size ceiling fan does James need for a room that has a square footage of 12 square meters and ceilings that are 3 meters tall?

   _____

   _____

   _____

Volume and Problem Solving (B)

Practice Finding Volumes of Composite Solids

Answer the questions.

1. Maria's dad pours a concrete patio that is 4 inches deep. When the concrete dries, it forms a composite solid. This diagram is the outline of the patio.

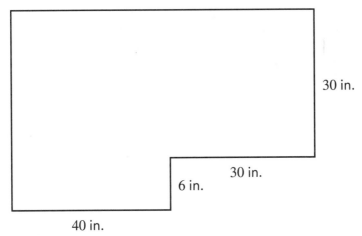

a. Draw a vertical line on the outline of the patio to divide it into 2 rectangles.

b. List the dimensions of the left side of the patio. Then, find the volume of the left side of the patio.

length = _____ width = _____ height = _____

left-side volume = _____

c. List the dimensions of the right side of the patio. Then, find the volume of the right side of the patio.

length = _____ width = _____ height = _____

right-side volume = _____

d. Add the left-side volume and right-side volume to find the total volume of the patio.

total volume = _____

Calculate the volume of the composite solid.

2. volume = _____

3. volume = _____

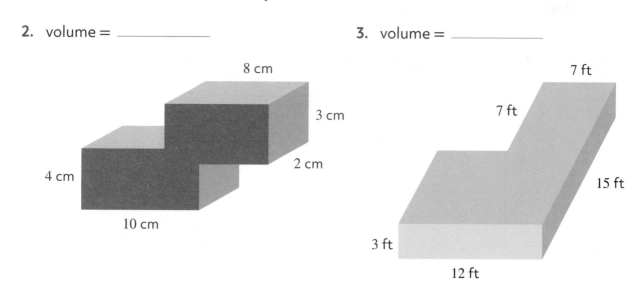

4. volume = _____

5. volume = _____

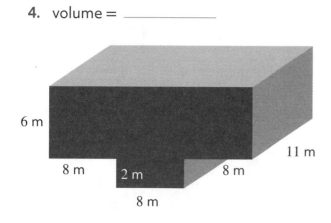

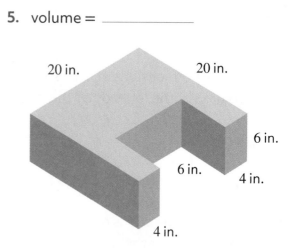

Practice Converting Between Forms of Numbers

Jessica is converting numbers with decimals between standard form and expanded form. Follow the instructions to help Jessica.

1. Jessica is converting 49.02 to expanded form. She begins by filling in a place value chart.

Ones			Decimals		
hundreds	tens	ones	tenths	hundredths	thousandths
	4	9	0	2	

   a. Write 49.02 in expanded form as a sum.

   49.02 = _____

   b. Rewrite the expanded form using products of powers of 10.

   49.02 = _____

2. Next, Jessica tries to write $(5 \times 100) + (4 \times 1) + \left(8 \times \frac{1}{10}\right) + 7 \times \frac{1}{1,000}$ in standard form.

   a. Multiply to evaluate inside each set of parentheses.

   _____

   b. Add to write the number in standard form. _____

Write the number in expanded form using products of powers of 10.

3. $1,608.2 =$ _____

4. $7.318 =$ _____

5. $240.08 =$ _____

6. $353.14 =$ _____

Write the number in standard form.

7. $6 \times 100 + 4 \times 1 + 8 \times \frac{1}{10} =$ _____

8. $6 \times 10 + 7 \times \frac{1}{10} + 9 \times \frac{1}{100} =$ _____

9. $5 \times 1 + 6 \times \frac{1}{10} + 7 \times \frac{1}{100} + 2 \times \frac{1}{1,000} =$ _____

10. $1 \times 1,000 + 7 \times 100 + 9 \times 1 + 5 \times \frac{1}{10} =$ _____

Decimals are everywhere!

Exploring Decimals (B)

Practice Reading and Writing Decimal Numbers

Answer the questions.

1. Matthew is trying to write the correct name for 12,688.67. He begins by writing the number in a place value chart.

Thousands			Ones			Decimals		
hundred thousands	ten thousands	thousands	hundreds	tens	ones	tenths	hundredths	thousandths
	1	2	6	8	8	6	7	

a. What is the correct name for the whole number part of the number?

_____

b. What word represents the decimal point? _____

c. What is the correct name for the decimal part of the number?

_____

d. What is the correct name for the number 12,688.67?

_____

2. Amelie writes that "two hundred and nine thousandths" is 0.209.

a. Amelie makes a mistake. What mistake does Amelie make?

_____

_____

b. What is the correct standard form of the number? _____

Write the correct name for the decimal number.

3. 7.099

_____

4. 236.1

_____

5. 0.824

_____

6. 8,361.03

_____

_____

Write the number in standard form.

7. six hundred four thousandths _____

8. six thousand nine hundred sixty and five tenths _____

9. three hundred eleven and eight hundredths _____

10. three and eight hundred ninety-four thousandths _____

Exploring Decimals (C)

Practice Plotting Decimals on a Number Line

Follow the steps to plot the number 1.403 on the number line.

1. This number line has 11 tick marks.

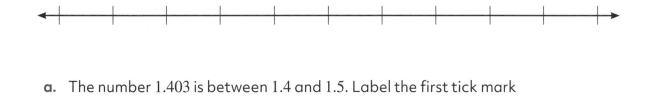

   a. The number 1.403 is between 1.4 and 1.5. Label the first tick mark 1.4 and the last tick mark 1.5.

   b. The number 1.403 is between 1.40 and 1.41. Label the second tick mark 1.41.

   c. The number 1.403 is partway between 1.40 and 1.41 but is closer to 1.40. Plot a point on the number line that is between 1.40 and 1.41 but is closer to 1.40. Label the point 1.403.

Plot and label the number on the number line.

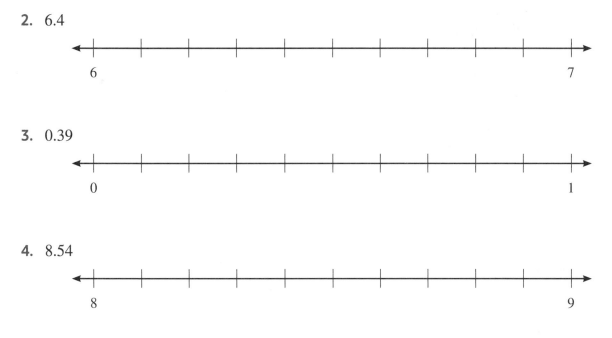

2. 6.4

6   7

3. 0.39

0   1

4. 8.54

8   9

5. 7.6

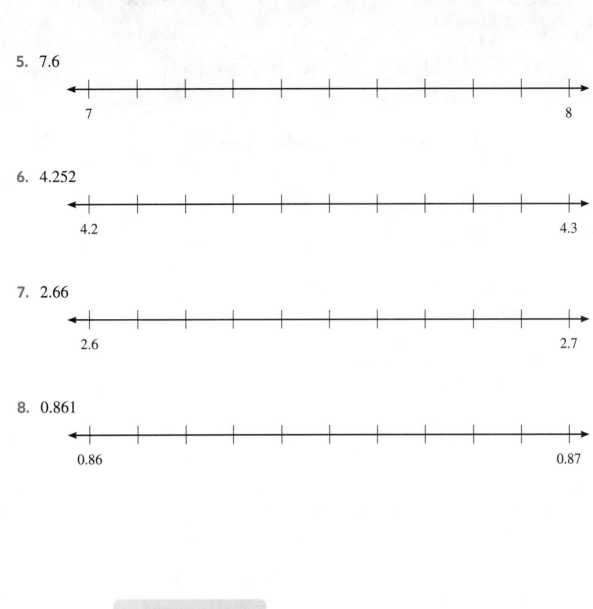

7   8

6. 4.252

4.2   4.3

7. 2.66

2.6   2.7

8. 0.861

0.86   0.87

Working with decimals is fun!

Practice Comparing Decimals Ending in the Same Place

Answer the questions.

1. Jordan is trying to use > and < to write two statements that compare 84.41 and 84.14.

    a. Write both numbers in the place value chart.

Ones			Decimals		
hundreds	tens	ones	tenths	hundredths	thousandths

    b. Start at the far-left place value position. Find the first pair of digits that differ. Compare them. Then, fill in the blanks to complete the statement.

    In the _____ place, _____ is greater than _____.

    c. Write a comparison statement using the numbers and >.

    _____

    d. Reverse the order of the numbers in the comparison statement and use <.

    _____

Write two statements to compare the numbers using > and <.

2. 11.75 and 11.88

_____

3. 2.104 and 2.164

_____

4. 287.7 and 287.1

_____

5. 38.66 and 38.61

_____

Compare the numbers using <, >, or =.

6. 4.348 ☐ 4.342

7. 15.92 ☐ 35.29

8. 0.698 ☐ 0.589

9. 172.8 ☐ 175.8

Can I always compare
two numbers using a > sign?

Comparing Decimals (B)

Practice Comparing Decimals Ending in Different Places

Answer the questions.

1. Three students compare 17.7 and 1.77. Each student writes a different comparison. Only one student is correct.

   a. Sarah determines that $17.7 < 1.77$ because $17.7 = 17.70$ and 77 hundredths is greater than 70 hundredths.

   Is Sarah correct? Why or why not?

   _____

   _____

   _____

   b. Matthew determines that $17.7 = 1.77$ because both numbers have three digits and all the digits are equal.

   Is Matthew correct? Why or why not?

   _____

   _____

   _____

   c. Evan determines that $17.7 > 1.77$ because 17 is greater than 1.

   Is Evan correct? Why or why not?

   _____

   _____

   _____

Compare the numbers using <, >, or =.

2. 3.15 ☐ 3.1

3. 0.11 ☐ 0.110

4. 1.471 ☐ 1.5

5. 9.1 ☐ 9.197

6. 7.664 ☐ 7.66

7. 10.3 ☐ 10.35

Solve. Write your answer as a complete sentence.

8. Aisha has two large dogs. Sandy weighs 50.2 pounds, and Mocca weighs 50.19 pounds.

   Which dog weighs less, or do they weigh the same amount?

   _____

9. Eric kicks a ball 34.62 meters. Jessica kicks a ball 34.7 meters.

   Who kicks the ball farther, or do they kick the ball the same distance?

   _____

10. James swims 32.9 laps. Eloise swims 32.90 laps.

    Who swims farther, or do they swim the same distance?

    _____

Rounding Decimals (A)

Practice Rounding Decimals to the Nearest Whole or Tenth

Answer the questions.

1. Min must round 8.163 to the nearest whole number and the nearest tenth.

   a. Which place value determines whether Min will round up or down

      to the nearest whole number? _____

   b. Should Min round up or down to the nearest whole number?
      Explain.

      _____

      _____

      _____

   c. What is 8.163 rounded to the nearest whole number? _____

   d. Which place value determines whether Min will round up or down

      to the nearest tenth? _____

   e. Should Min round up or down to the nearest tenth? Explain.

      _____

      _____

      _____

   f. What is 8.163 rounded to the nearest tenth? _____

Round the decimal number to the given place value.

2. 65.7 to the nearest whole number _____

3. 0.31 to the nearest tenth _____

4. 4.773 to the nearest tenth _____

5. 59.86 to the nearest whole number _____

6. 5.122 to the nearest whole number _____

Solve by rounding to the given place value.

7. Maria keeps a record of the amount of gasoline she buys for her lawn-mowing service. Her records show that she bought 138.93 gallons of gasoline this summer.

   About how many gallons of gas did Maria buy this summer, rounded

   to the nearest tenth of a gallon? _____

Rounding can be useful in cooking.

Rounding Decimals (B)

Practice Rounding to the Hundredths and Thousandths Places

Fill in the blanks to complete the statement.

1. Round 3.2906 to different place values.

    a. The digit to the right of the decimal point is _____ ,

    so 3.2906 rounded to the nearest **whole number** is _____ .

    b. The digit to the right of the tenths place is _____ ,

    so 3.2906 rounded to the nearest **tenth** is _____ .

    c. The digit to the right of the hundredths place is _____ ,

    so 3.2906 rounded to the nearest **hundredth** is _____ .

    d. The digit to the right of the thousandths place is _____ ,

    so 3.2906 rounded to the nearest **thousandth** is _____ .

Round the decimal number to the given place value.

2. 5.9847 to the nearest hundredth _____

3. 74.71762 to the nearest thousandth _____

4. 0.0212 to the nearest thousandth _____

5. 6.83186 to the nearest hundredth _____

6. 40.3552 to the nearest thousandth _____

7. 631.74677 to the nearest hundredth _____

Solve by rounding to the given place value.

8. The gas pump shows that Jordan bought 16.571 gallons of gas. About how many gallons of gas did Jordan buy, rounded to the nearest hundredth of a gallon? _____

With a little practice, I can be a rounding expert.

Place Value Relationships to Thousandths (A)

Practice Comparing a Digit to a Like Digit to Its Right

Fill in the blanks to complete the statement.

1. What are the rules for comparing a digit with a like digit to its right?

    a. The value of a digit is _____ times the value of a like digit one place to its right.

    b. The value of a digit is _____ times the value of a like digit two places to its right.

    c. The value of a digit is _____ times the value of a like digit three places to its right.

2. How do the values of the 8s in the number 138.809 compare?

    The value of the _____ in the ones place is _____ times

    the value of the _____ in the tenths place.

3. How do the values of the 3s in 31.809 and 7,042.03 compare?

    The value of the 3 in 31.809 is _____ times the value of

    the 3 in 7,042.03 because the hundredths place is _____ places
    to the right of the tens place.

Write a statement to answer the question.

4. How do the values of the 9s in 0.921 and 0.296 compare?

_____

_____

5. How do the values of the 6s in the number 60.16 compare?

_____

_____

6. How do the values of the 3s in 34.97 and 56.39 compare?

_____

_____

7. How do the values of the 4s in the number 54,134.7 compare?

_____

_____

8. How do the values of the 7s in the number 1.877 compare?

_____

_____

9. How do the values of the 5s in 598 and 745 compare?

_____

_____

Place Value Relationships to Thousandths (B)

Practice Comparing Values of Like Digits

Rami compares the 4 in the thousandths place of 14.804 to the 4 in the ones place. Here is Rami's comparison:

> The 4 in the thousandths place is 1,000 times the value of the 4 in the ones place of 14.804.

1. Rami's statement is **not** correct.

   a. What mistake does Rami make?

   _____

   _____

   b. What is the correct relationship between the 4 in the thousandths place and the 4 in the ones place?

   _____

   _____

   c. What is another way to express the relationship between the two 4s in 14.804?

   _____

   _____

Write a statement to answer the question.

2. How does the 8 in the thousandths place compare to the 8 in the tenths place of 0.858?

   _____

3. How does the value of the 4 in the number 34.9 compare to the value of the 4 in the number 249?

_____

_____

4. How does the value of the 6 in the number 6.19 compare to the 6 in the number 627.3?

_____

_____

5. How does the 9 in the thousandths place compare to the 9 in the ones place of 79.839?

_____

_____

Write two statements to answer the question.

6. How do the values of the 7s in 0.72 and 0.97 compare?

_____

_____

_____

7. How do the values of the 3s in the number 3,813 compare?

_____

_____

_____

Decimal Addition (A)

Practice Adding Decimals to Tenths

Use the model to find the sum.

1. $0.6 + 0.8$

   a. Shade the grids to model the sum.

   b. What is the sum of 0.6 and 0.8? _____

2. $1.5 + 2.7$

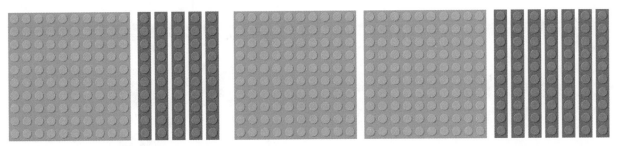

   a. The model shows a total of _____ wholes and _____ tenths.

   After regrouping, there are _____ wholes and _____ tenths.

   b. What is the sum of 1.5 and 2.7? _____

3. $1.1 + 0.4$

    a. Draw jumps on the number line to model the sum.

    0.0 0.1 0.2 0.3 0.4 0.5 0.6 0.7 0.8 0.9 1.0 1.1 1.2 1.3 1.4 1.5 1.6 1.7 1.8 1.9 2.0

    b. What is the sum of 1.1 and 0.4? _____

Estimate the sum by rounding each number to the nearest whole. Then, find the actual sum.

4. $12.7 + 3.2$

    a. estimate: _____

    b. sum: _____

5. $4.3 + 0.8 + 11.5$

    a. estimate: _____

    b. sum: _____

Add.

6. $15.3 + 7.2$ _____

7. $105 + 30.7$ _____

8. $19.6 + 8.7$ _____

9. $4.4 + 0.8 + 6.7$ _____

10. $55.3 + 21.1$ _____

11. $94.2 + 6.8$ _____

Practice Adding Decimals to Hundredths

Use the model to find the sum.

1. $1.3 + 1.46$

    a. Shade the grids to model the sum.

    b. What is the sum of 1.3 and 1.46? _____

2. $1.35 + 1.28$

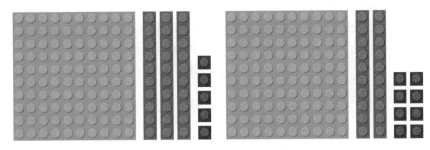

    a. The model shows a total of _____ wholes, _____ tenths, and

        _____ hundredths. After regrouping, there are _____ wholes,

        _____ tenths, and _____ hundredths.

    b. What is the sum of 1.35 and 1.28? _____

Estimate the sum by rounding each number to the nearest whole.
Then, find the actual sum.

3. $3.75 + 1.2 + 6.9$

    a. estimate: _____

    b. sum: _____

4. $52.3 + 71.68$

    a. estimate: _____

    b. sum: _____

Add.

5. $2.36 + 9.02$ _____

6. $0.71 + 5.04$ _____

7. $42.3 + 96.67$ _____

8. $31.32 + 7.5 + 0.04$ _____

9. $80.38 + 267.56$ _____

10. $4.92 + 10.1$ _____

11. $0.8 + 0.88 + 8$ _____

12. $7{,}007.45 + 110.66$ _____

Decimal Subtraction (A)

Practice Subtracting Decimals to Tenths

Use the model to find the difference.

1. 2.3 − 1.4

   a. Shade the grids to model 2.3. Then, cross out 1.4.

   b. What is the difference of 2.3 and 1.4? _____

2. 1.4 − 0.6

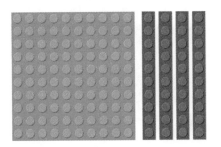

   a. The model shows 1 whole and 4 tenths. You cannot take 6 tenths away from

      4 tenths, so regroup the whole into _____ tenths. You then have

      _____ tenths. After removing 6 tenths, there are _____ tenths left.

   b. What is the difference of 1.4 and 0.6? _____

3. 2 − 1.2

    a. Draw a jump or jumps on the number line to model the difference.

    0.0 0.1 0.2 0.3 0.4 0.5 0.6 0.7 0.8 0.9 1.0 1.1 1.2 1.3 1.4 1.5 1.6 1.7 1.8 1.9 2.0

    b. What is the difference of 2 and 1.2? _____

Estimate the difference by rounding each number to the nearest whole. Then, find the actual difference.

4. 57.4 − 4.3

    a. estimate: _____

    b. difference: _____

5. 18.6 − 3.8

    a. estimate: _____

    b. difference: _____

Subtract.

6. 20.5 − 8.3 _____

7. 5.2 − 0.4 _____

8. 710.5 − 495.3 _____

9. 391.2 − 18.8 _____

10. 10.6 − 7.6 _____

11. 63 − 55.1 _____

Practice Subtracting Decimals to Hundredths

Use the model to find the difference.

1. 1.8 − 0.52

   a. Shade the grids to model 1.8. Then, cross out 0.52.

   b. What is the difference of 1.8 and 0.52? _____

2. 2.71 − 1.83

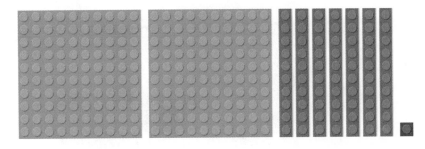

   a. The model shows 2 wholes, 7 tenths, and 1 hundredth. You cannot take
      3 hundredths away from 1 hundredth, so regroup 1 tenth into 10 hundredths.

      You then have 2 wholes, _____ tenths, and _____ hundredths.

      You cannot take 8 tenths away from _____ tenths, so regroup 1 whole into

      10 tenths. You then have 1 whole, _____ tenths, and _____ hundredths.

   b. What is the difference of 2.71 and 1.83? _____

Estimate the difference by rounding each number to the nearest whole. Then, find the actual difference.

3. 8.24 − 1.95

    a. estimate: _____

    b. difference: _____

4. 17.6 − 5.35

    a. estimate: _____

    b. difference: _____

Subtract.

5. 3.08 − 2.37 _____

6. 26.89 − 3.4 _____

7. 64.6 − 24.05 _____

8. 304.01 − 138.42 _____

9. 62 − 4.77 _____

10. 798.38 − 212.5 _____

11. 5.4 − 0.39 _____

12. 50.36 − 2.99 _____

Add and Subtract Decimals in the Real World (A)

Practice Solving Real-World Money Problems

At the art store, Jada is buying a poster board for $0.65, glitter for $3.29, and glue for $1.99.

1. Is it reasonable for Jada to think that she can pay for all three items with a $5 bill? Explain.

_____

_____

_____

2. What is the total cost of the three items? _____

Write the addition or subtraction expression that can be used to answer the question. Then, answer the question.

3. After Evan's mom gives him $3.25, Evan has $7.18. How much money did Evan have before his mom gave him money?

   a. expression: _____

   b. answer: _____

4. At the pet store, Amelie buys a bag of cat treats for $2.39 and a cat toy for $0.71. How much does Amelie spend at the pet store?

   a. expression: _____

   b. answer: _____

Answer the question.

5. Rami buys a bottle of water for $1.63.

   How much change does he get back from a $5 bill? _____

6. Juan and Kiki empty their piggy banks. Juan has $12.08 in change, and Kiki has $7.29 in change.

   How much more money does Juan have than Kiki? _____

7. Sarah has $0.46 in her pocket and $0.98 in her purse.

   How much money does Sarah have altogether? _____

8. To get to the zoo, Min's family spends $10.90 to ride the train and then $4.10 to ride the bus.

   How much does it cost Min's family to get to the zoo? _____

9. For lunch, Maria buys a ham sandwich for $4.30, a bag of chips for $1.38, and a carton of chocolate milk for $0.85.

   How much does Maria's lunch cost? _____

10. Before Eric's brother borrows money from him, Eric has $9.60. After Eric's brother borrows the money, Eric has $2.25.

    How much money does Eric's brother borrow? _____

> I can solve money problems.

Add and Subtract Decimals in the Real World (B)

Practice Adding and Subtracting Decimals in the Real World

Matthew catches a fish that weighs 7.25 pounds. His dad catches a fish that weighs 1.3 pounds less than Matthew's fish.

1. Matthew's sister says, "That means dad's fish weighs 7.12 pounds."
   Is her statement reasonable? Explain.

   _____

   _____

   _____

2. How much does Matthew's dad's fish weigh? _____

Write the addition or subtraction expression that can be used to answer the question. Then, answer the question.

3. Eloise's family buys 2 bags of apples. One bag weighs 3.19 pounds.
   The other bag weighs 4.05 pounds.

   How many pounds of apples does Eloise's family buy?

   a. expression: _____

   b. answer: _____

4. In an arcade game, Matthew scores his first basket 2.8 seconds
   faster than it takes Jessica to score her first basket. It takes Jessica
   9.1 seconds to score her first basket.

   How long does it take Matthew to score his first basket?

   a. expression: _____

   b. answer: _____

Answer the question.

5. On a 2-day road trip, Aisha's family travels 303.2 miles the first day and 277.5 miles the second day.

   How far does her family travel on the trip? _____

6. A car's gas tank can hold up to 18.15 gallons of gas. The last time the car was at the gas station, it took 14.58 gallons of gas to fill the tank.

   How much gas was in the tank before it was filled? _____

7. The temperature of a liquid begins at 74.2°F and then increases by 9.76°F.

   What is the liquid's temperature after the increase? _____

8. The longest snake in a zoo is 4.1 meters long. This length is 3.15 meters longer than the shortest snake in the zoo.

   What is the length of the zoo's shortest snake? _____

9. Juan's cactus was 12.38 centimeters tall when he bought it. It has grown 19 centimeters since he bought it.

   How tall is Juan's cactus now? _____

10. A camp leader brings a container of 22.4 liters of water to a campsite. Natalie is the first camper to use the leader's water when she fills up a dishpan with 4.25 liters of water.

   How much water is in the camp leader's container after Natalie fills

   the dishpan? _____

Add and Subtract Decimals in the Real World (C)

Practice Solving Multistep, Real-World Problems with Decimals

Kiki has $2.48 in her change purse and $1.69 in her hand. Jordan has $3.05 in his left pocket and $1.09 in his right pocket.

1. How much money does Kiki have in all? _____

2. How much money does Jordan have in all? _____

3. Who has more money, and how much more money do that person have?

   _____

   _____

Create a real-world problem using the description.
Then, solve the problem.

4. Create a two-step problem (one addition and one subtraction) that uses these amounts: $5, $2.46, and $0.70.

   a. problem: _____

   _____

   _____

   _____

   b. answer: _____

5. Create a three-step problem (two addition and one subtraction) that uses these amounts: 6.32, 4.9, 3.15, and 5.58.

   a. problem: _____

   _____

   _____

   _____

   b. answer: _____

Answer the question.

6. Jessica leaves the house with $8.63. She spends $0.75 to ride the bus and then $2.30 on a popsicle. While walking home, she finds a quarter.

   How much money does Jessica have when she gets home? _____

7. A construction worker needs 29 pounds of cement. He has 13.2 pounds of cement on his truck, and his boss says there are 10.9 pounds of cement in a wheelbarrow.

   How much more cement does the construction worker need? _____

8. James and Matthew go to the mall. James takes $14.15 and buys a belt for $11.39. Matthew takes $10 and buys a poster for $4.83 and a goldfish for $2.99. They combine their change to buy a popcorn that costs $4.39. They toss the rest of their money into a fountain for charity.

   How much money do James and Matthew toss into the fountain? _____

9. In a video game, it takes Natalie 48.23 seconds to find the magic key and then 30.7 seconds to take the key through the maze. When Jada plays, it takes her 1.06 seconds longer than Natalie to find the key, but she finishes the maze 2.82 seconds faster than Natalie.

   How long does it take Jada to find the key and go through the maze? _____

Multiplying Whole Numbers by Decimals (A)

Practice Using Models to Multiply Wholes by Decimals

Use the model to find the product.

1. 4×0.26

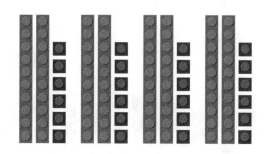

a. There are 8 tenths and 24 hundredths. After regrouping hundredths into tenths,

there are _____ tenths and _____ hundredths. After regrouping

tenths into wholes, there are _____ whole, _____ tenths, and

_____ hundredths.

b. What is the product of 4 and 0.26? _____

2. 3×0.43

a. Shade the grids to model the product.

b. What is the product of 3 and 0.43? _____

3. 6×0.2

   a. Draw jumps on the number line to model the product.

   0.0 0.1 0.2 0.3 0.4 0.5 0.6 0.7 0.8 0.9 1.0 1.1 1.2 1.3 1.4 1.5 1.6 1.7 1.8 1.9 2.0

   b. What is the product of 6 and 0.2? _____

4. 1.08×3

   What is the product of 1.08 and 3? _____

5. 0.65×2

   a. Shade the grids to model the product.

   b. What is the product of 0.65 and 2? _____

Multiplying Whole Numbers by Decimals (B)

Practice Using the Algorithm to Multiply Wholes by Decimals

Answer the questions.

1. Aisha multiplies 12 by 0.8 as shown.

$$\begin{array}{r} \overset{1}{12} \\ \times\, 0.8 \\ \hline 0.96 \end{array}$$

   a. What part of the multiplication algorithm does Aisha do correctly?

   _____

   _____

   b. What part of the multiplication algorithm does Aisha do incorrectly?

   _____

   _____

   c. Give the correct product and explain how you determined it.

   _____

   _____

2. James multiplies 79 by 3.21 and gets 253.59. He's not sure if he puts
   the decimal point in the correct spot. Explain how James can use
   estimation to confirm his placement of the decimal point.

   _____

   _____

   _____

Multiply.

3.
$$\begin{array}{r} 2.05 \\ \times\ \ 63 \\ \hline \end{array}$$

4.
$$\begin{array}{r} 97 \\ \times\ \ 3.2 \\ \hline \end{array}$$

5.
$$\begin{array}{r} 430 \\ \times\ \ 1.24 \\ \hline \end{array}$$

6. 88×17.6 _____

7. 12.34×3 _____

8. 8.9×36 _____

9. 164×3.08 _____

10. 15.05×41 _____

11. $2{,}493 \times 61.7$ _____

Multiplying Whole Numbers by Decimals (C)

Practice Multiplying Wholes by Decimals in the Real World

Answer the questions.

1. Juan and Amelie begin a water-balloon toss standing 3 feet away from each other.

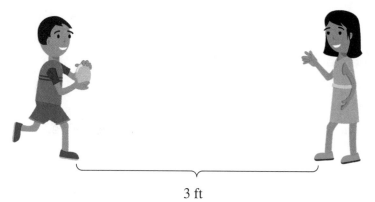

3 ft

    a. Every time a player catches a balloon without popping it, both players take one step back. Each step back is 1.25 feet long.

    How much farther apart are the players after each successful catch?

    _____

    b. Juan and Amelie have 5 successful catches before the balloon pops. Write and solve a multiplication problem to find how much farther apart they are when the balloon pops than when they begin the toss.

    _____

    c. How far apart are Juan and Amelie when the balloon pops?

    _____

2. Min carries a dozen books. Each book weighs 0.7 kilogram.

   How much do all the books weigh? _____

3. One inch is the same as 2.54 centimeters. A shoelace is 45 inches long.

   How many centimeters long is the shoelace? _____

4. A store buys T-shirts for $3.30 and sells them for 4 times as much.

   How much does the store sell the T-shirts for? _____

5. The label on a rug shows that it is 8 feet long and 5.75 feet wide.

   What is the area of the rug? _____

6. Jessica buys 33 beads to make a necklace. Each bead costs $0.16.

   How much does Jessica spend on beads for her necklace? _____

7. A theater has 40 rows of seats. There are 22 seats in each row. It costs
   $2.79 to deep clean each seat.

   How much does it cost to deep clean all the seats in the theater? _____

8. Jada bikes to her grandfather's home and back again, 3 times a week
   for 15 weeks. The distance between her home and her grandfather's
   home is 1.7 kilometers.

   How far does Jada bike in all? _____

Practice Explaining How to Multiply a Decimal by Powers of 10

Answer the question.

1. When Earth and Mars are closest to each other, they are about 5.46×10^7 kilometers apart. Raj says, "To write this number in standard form, I can remove the decimal point and add 7 zeros to 5.46, so the distance is 5,460,000,000 kilometers." Explain and correct Raj's error.

_____

_____

_____

_____

2. When Earth and Mars are farthest from each other, they are about $4.01 \times 100{,}000{,}000$ kilometers apart. Sarah says, "To write this number in standard form, I can move the decimal point nine places to the right because there are 9 digits in the 100,000,000." Explain and correct Sarah's error.

_____

_____

_____

_____

3. The number 1 can be written as 10^0. Explain how this makes sense with what you know about multiplying a number by 1.

_____

_____

_____

_____

4. Juan solves a multiplication problem by moving the decimal point in 0.02 five places to the right. What is the second factor in Juan's multiplication problem? Explain how you know.

_____

_____

_____

Fill in the blank to complete the statement.

5. The distance around the earth's equator can be written as $24.9 \times 1,000$ miles. To multiply 24.9 by 1,000, move the decimal point

_____ places to the right.

6. The earth's volume is about 2.6×10^{11} cubic miles. To multiply 2.6 by

10^{11}, move the decimal point _____ places to the right.

7. Weather satellites are in an orbit about $0.36 \times 100,000$ kilometers above the earth's surface. To multiply 0.36 by 100,000, move the

decimal point _____ places to the right.

Multiplying Decimals by Powers of 10 (B)

Practice Multiplying Decimals by Powers of 10

The moon is in an orbit around the earth, and the length of this orbit is $3.844 \times 100{,}000$ kilometers.

1. What is the shortcut for multiplying 3.844 by 100,000?

   _____

   _____

2. Write the length of the moon's orbit so that the number is in standard form.

   _____

Multiply.

3. $7.3 \times 1{,}000{,}000$ _____

4. $0.0085 \times 10{,}000$ _____

5. 19.492×10^{7} _____

6. 0.1×10^{4} _____

7. $105.67 \times 100{,}000$ _____

8. 3.49×10^{6} _____

9. $18.25 × 1,000 _____

10. $20.03 × 10 _____

Determine the missing factor. Write powers of 10 without exponents.

11. [ ] $\times 10^3 = 61{,}500$

12. [ ] $\times 100 = 330$

13. $14.902 \times$ [ ] $= 14{,}902{,}000$

14. $0.0022 \times$ [ ] $= 220$

The stars are so far away!

Multiplying Two Decimals (A)

Practice Multiplying Decimals to Tenths

Use the model to find the product.

1. 2.4×0.7

   a. Shade the grids to model the product.

   b. There are _____ tenths and _____ hundredths. After

   regrouping hundredths into tenths, there are _____ tenths and

   _____ hundredths. After regrouping tenths into wholes, there are 1 whole,

   _____ tenths, and _____ hundredths.

   c. What is the product of 2.4 and 0.7? _____

Answer the question.

2. To find 13.1×46.5, Evan correctly multiplies the numbers as if they are whole numbers and gets 60915 in the last line.

   How can Evan use estimation to determine the correct position for the decimal point?

   _____

   _____

3. How can you estimate the product of 0.5 and 2.9?

_____

_____

_____

Multiply.

4. 1.8×2.3 _____

5. 54.6×9.2 _____

6. 105.3×0.7 _____

> Doing math makes me feel like dancing!

7. 218.5×13.6 _____

8. $15.5 - 2.4 \times 4.9$ _____

9. $15.3 \times 3.7 + 9.6 \times 0.8$ _____

Multiplying Two Decimals (B)

Practice Multiplying Decimals to Tenths and Hundredths

Use the model to find the product.

1. 0.5×0.35

   a. Shade the grid to represent the product.

   b. How many thousandths are shaded? _____

   c. What is the product of 0.5 and 0.35? _____

Answer the question.

2. To find 9.41×2.7, Eloise correctly multiplies the numbers as if they are whole numbers and gets 25407 in the last line.

   How can Eloise use estimation to determine the correct position for the decimal point?

   _____

   _____

   _____

3. Juan is told that the product of 12.02 and 7.5 is 90.15. Juan says, "That cannot be correct, because there should be three digits after the decimal point."

What would you say to Juan about his response?

_____

_____

_____

_____

Multiply.

4. 5.2×13.43 _____

5. 0.06×0.2 _____

6. 214.78×5.5 _____

7. 6.3×2.49 _____

8. $8.08 + 1.05 \times 0.6$ _____

9. $5.04 \times 1.8 + 6$ _____

> Multiplying decimals isn't hard at all.

Multiplying Two Decimals (C)

Practice Multiplying Decimals to Hundredths

Use the model to find the product.

1. 0.75×0.55

   a. Shade the grid to represent the product.

   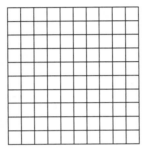

   b. Determine the number of ten-thousandths shaded.

   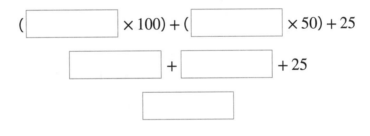

   $$(\boxed{} \times 100) + (\boxed{} \times 50) + 25$$

   $$\boxed{} + \boxed{} + 25$$

   $$\boxed{}$$

   c. What is the product of 0.75 and 0.55? _____

Answer the question.

2. To find 3.24×18.91, Eric correctly multiplies the numbers as if they are whole numbers and gets 612684 in the last line.

   How can Eric use estimation to determine the correct position for the decimal point?

   _____

   _____

3. How can you estimate the product of 0.48 and 13.72?

_____

_____

_____

Multiply.

4. 0.08×0.05 _____

5. 2.07×6.51 _____

6. 11.33×4.05 _____

7. 67.35×8.14 _____

8. $7.2 + 1.31 \times 2.48$ _____

9. $0.21 \times 0.97 - 0.2$ _____

I'm pretty good at multiplying decimals.

Multiplying Two Decimals (D)

Practice Multiplying Decimals in the Real World

Answer the questions.

1. James's dad buys 36.25 feet of rope for his boat. The rope costs $0.27 per foot.

   a. How much does the rope cost? _____

   b. James's dad pays for the rope with a $20 bill. How much change

   does he get back? _____

Create a real-world multiplication problem using the numbers. Then, solve the problem.

2. numbers: 2.3 and 1.5.

   a. problem: _____

   _____

   _____

   _____

   b. answer: _____

3. numbers: 14.25 and 6.75.

   a. problem: _____

   _____

   _____

   b. answer: _____

Explain how to use estimation to determine whether the statement is reasonable.

4. A plant grows 22.8 centimeters each year. Therefore, the plant will grow 57 centimeters in 2.5 years.

_____

_____

_____

5. A kiddie ride at an amusement park lasts 3.35 minutes. Cars on the ride travel 118.2 meters per minute. Therefore, cars on the ride travel 3,959.7 meters during the ride.

_____

_____

_____

Answer the question.

6. Maria collects 8.56 pounds of aluminum cans for recycling. She gets paid $0.37 per pound.

   How much money does Maria get for the cans? _____

7. The water temperature at the start of an experiment is 73.8°F. During the experiment, the temperature rises 1.2°F every minute for 11.4 minutes.

   What is the water temperature at the end of the experiment? _____

8. A certain type of tile costs $4.69 per square foot.

   How much would it cost to cover a rectangular area that is 7.5 feet long

   and 5 feet wide with this tile? _____

Dividing Whole Numbers and Decimals (A)

Practice Dividing Wholes by Decimals

Use the model to find the quotient.

1. $4 \div 0.8$

   a. Draw loops on the figure to model the quotient.

   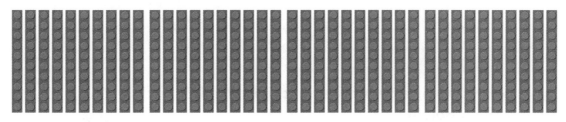

   b. What is the quotient of 4 and 0.8? _____

2. $4 \div 0.25$

   a. Draw jumps on the number line to model the quotient.

   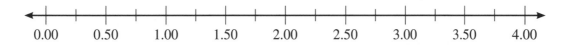

   b. What is the quotient of 4 and 0.25? _____

Answer the questions.

3. Sarah will put $0.15 in her new piggy bank every week until she has $6 in the bank.

   How many weeks it will take her to save $6?

   Write and solve a division problem to find out. _____

4. A factory has 10 pounds of red dye for its marbles. Each batch of marbles uses 0.2 pound of red dye.

    a. Juan says that the factory can make 5 batches of marbles with the 10 pounds of dye. Explain why his statement is not reasonable.

    _____

    _____

    _____

    b. How many batches of marbles can the factory make? _____

Create a real-world division problem that fits the description. Then, solve the problem.

5. Divide 21 by 0.7.

    a. problem: _____

    _____

    _____

    b. answer: _____

6. Divide $30 by $0.75.

    a. problem: _____

    _____

    b. answer: _____

Dividing Whole Numbers and Decimals (B)

Practice Dividing Decimals by Wholes

Use the model to find the quotient.

1. 3.72 ÷ 3

  a. After putting 1 whole and _____ tenths into each of three groups, you have 1 tenth and 2 hundredths remaining. Regroup

     the tenth into 10 hundredths to have _____ hundredths. Put an equal number of hundredths into each group. You now have 1 whole,

     _____ tenths, and _____ hundredths in each group.

  b. What is the quotient of 3.72 and 3? _____

2. 1.2 ÷ 3

  a. Draw jumps on the number line to model the quotient.

  b. What is the quotient of 1.2 and 3? _____

Answer the questions.

3. Natalie's sister saves $148.20 by saving the same amount of money each week for 52 weeks.

   a. Natalie says, "You must have saved about 30 cents each week." Explain why Natalie's statement is **not** reasonable.

   _____

   _____

   b. How much money does Natalie's sister save each week? _____

4. A cricket jumps 7 times in a row, and each jump is the same length. The cricket jumps a total of 5.25 feet.

   How far is each jump? Write and solve a division problem to find out.

   _____

Create a real-world division problem that fits the description. Then, solve the problem.

5. Divide 80.7 by 3.

   a. problem: _____

   _____

   _____

   b. answer: _____

6. Divide $18.54 by 9.

   a. problem: _____

   _____

   b. answer: _____

Dividing Whole Numbers and Decimals (C)

Practice Dividing a Whole by a Greater Whole

Use the model to find the quotient.

1. $2 \div 8$

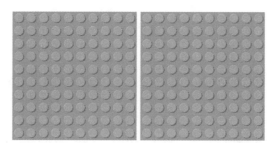

    a. Regroup each whole into _____ hundredths for a total

    of _____ hundredths. When you divide these hundredths into

    8 equal groups, you have _____ hundredths in each group.

    b. What is the quotient of 2 and 8? _____

2. $3 \div 4$

    a. Draw jumps on the number line to model the quotient.

    b. What is the quotient of 3 and 4? _____

Answer the question.

3. How is $3 \div 10$ different than $10 \div 3$?

_____

_____

_____

_____

4. Fifteen children split $9 among themselves so that each child receives
   the same amount.

   How much does each child receive? Write and solve a division problem to find out.

   _____

5. At an art camp, 15 children each get an equal amount of the
   12 pounds of sand that are in a bin. Kiki is one of those children.
   She uses 0.5 pound of her sand for her first art project.

   How much sand does Kiki have left over for her second art project?

   _____

Divide.

6. $20\overline{)3}$

7. $30\overline{)12}$

8. $50\overline{)44}$

9. $8\overline{)1}$

Dividing Decimals by Powers of 10 (A)

Practice Explaining How to Divide a Decimal by Powers of 10

Answer the question.

1. A bakery uses 33.2 pounds of flour to make 1,000 hot dog buns. Min says, "To determine how many pounds of flour are in one bun, divide 33.2 by 1,000. The shortcut is to add 3 zeros to the left side of the number, so each bun has 0.000332 pound of flour in it." Explain and correct Min's error.

    _____

    _____

    _____

2. A local playground is rectangular and has an area of 76.5 square meters. One side of the playground is 10 meters long. Maria says, "The length of the other side is the quotient of 76.5 and 10, so move the decimal point in 76.5 two places to the left because there are two digits in the number 10." Explain and correct Maria's error.

    _____

    _____

    _____

    _____

3. When multiplying and dividing by powers of 10, when do you move the decimal point to the right and when do you move the decimal point to the left?

_____

_____

_____

4. Evan correctly divides 1.35 by a power of 10 to get 0.00000135. What power of 10 does Evan divide by? Explain how you know.

_____

_____

_____

Fill in the blank to complete the statement.

5. To divide 340.025 by 100, move the decimal point _____ places to the left.

6. To divide 0.08 by 10^4, move the decimal point _____ places to the left.

7. To divide 22,906.45 by 100,000, move the decimal point _____ places to the left.

8. To divide 6,933.9 by 10 million, move the decimal point _____ places to the left.

Practice Dividing Decimals by Powers of 10

Answer the questions.

1. A mega gumball machine at an amusement park is filled with 10,000 gumballs. The gumballs weigh 86.2 kilograms altogether.

   a. To determine the weight of one gumball in the machine, Evan will divide. What is the shortcut for dividing 86.2 by 10,000?

   _____

   _____

   b. What is the weight of one gumball? _____

2. The height of the Statue of Liberty, from the heel to the top of the head, is 111.5 feet.

   a. Eloise has a model of the Statue of Liberty that is $\frac{1}{100}$ the height of the actual statue. What division problem can be solved to

   determine the height of Eloise's model? _____

   b. What is the height of Eloise's model? _____

3. Matthew buys a pack of 10 colored pencils for $0.92. He writes, "I would need $0.092 to buy one more pencil." What is wrong with Matthew's statement?

   _____

   _____

   _____

4. In the equation $n \div 1{,}000 = 0.01572$, what number does the letter

   n represent? _____

Divide.

5. $0.8 \div 10^3$ _____

6. $412.39 \div 100$ _____

7. $715{,}249.58 \div 10^5$ _____

Oh no! I moved the decimal point the wrong way.

8. $\$3.30 \div 10$ _____

Decimal Division (A)

Practice Dividing Decimals to Tenths

Use the model to find the quotient.

1. $0.1 \div 0.5$

   a. Shade the grid to form a rectangle with an area of 0.1 and a side that measures 0.5.

   b. What is the quotient of 0.1 and 0.5? _____

2. $2.4 \div 0.3$

   a. Draw jumps on the number line to model the quotient.

   0.0   0.2   0.4   0.6   0.8   1.0   1.2   1.4   1.6   1.8   2.0   2.2   2.4   2.6   2.8   3.0

   b. What is the quotient of 2.4 and 0.3? _____

I can divide decimals!

Answer the questions.

3. The temperature of a liquid in an experiment increases 44.2°F in 5.2 minutes. The temperature increases at a steady rate.

   a. Explain how to estimate the number of degrees the temperature increases every minute.

   _____

   _____

   _____

   b. How many degrees does the temperature increase every minute? _____

4. Create and solve a real-world problem that requires dividing 14.7 by 1.4.

   _____

   _____

   _____

5. A carpenter has a piece of wood that is 12.5 feet long. She needs to divide it into pieces that are each 2.5 feet long. How many pieces can she make? Write and solve a division

   problem to find out. _____

6. Jordan's bike weighs 18.9 pounds. His bike weighs 3.5 times as much as his puppy.

   How much does Jordan's puppy weigh? _____

7. Jada buys 67.2 meters of string to make string bracelets and uses 4.2 yards for each bracelet. Jessica buys 75.4 meters of string to make string bracelets and uses 5.8 yards for each bracelet.

   Who can make more bracelets? _____

   How many more bracelets can she make? _____

Decimal Division (B)

Practice Dividing Hundredths by Tenths

Use the model to find the quotient of 0.42 and 0.6.

1. Shade the grid to form a rectangle with an area of 0.42 and a side that measures 0.6.

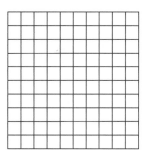

2. What is the quotient of 0.42 and 0.6? _____

Answer the questions.

3. An employee who earns a set amount of money per hour earns $172.55 for 8.5 hours of work.

   a. Explain how to estimate the amount of money the employee gets paid per hour.

   _____

   _____

   _____

   _____

   b. How much does the employee get paid per hour? _____

4. Create and solve a real-world problem that requires dividing 20.75 by 2.5.

_____

_____

_____

_____

5. A homeowner pays $13.75 for 2.2 cubic yards of crushed rock to use for landscaping his yard.

   How much does 1 cubic yard of the crushed rock cost? Write and solve a division problem to find out.

   _____

6. Amelie pays $10.73 for 3.7 pounds of cherries.

   What is the cost for 1 pound of cherries? _____

7. A construction team builds a brick wall in 2 weeks. At the end of the first week, the wall is 3.6 meters high. During the second week, the team makes the wall 2.25 meters higher. The final height of the wall is 1.3 times the originally planned height.

   How tall was the wall originally going to be?

   _____

Decimal Division (C)

Practice Dividing Hundredths by Hundredths

Use the model to find the quotient of 0.36 and 0.45.

1. Shade the grid to form a rectangle with an area of 0.36 and a side that measures 0.45.

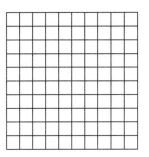

2. What is the quotient of 0.36 and 0.45? _____

Answer the questions.

3. Sarah needs to divide 25.01 by 0.82.

   a. How could Sarah estimate the quotient?

   _____

   _____

   _____

   _____

   b. What is the quotient of 25.01 and 0.82? _____

4. Create and solve a real-world problem that requires dividing $2.55 by $0.15.

_____

_____

_____

_____

5. Evan spends $4.06 on magnets. The magnets cost $0.58 each.

   How many magnets does Evan buy? Write and solve a division problem to find out.

   _____

6. Sarah rides a stationary bike at a steady speed. The display indicates that she bikes for 0.35 hour and covers a distance of 1.68 miles.

   What is her speed in miles per hour? _____

7. A chef spends $1.12 buying salt for $0.32 per pound. He uses 1.25 pounds of that salt.

   How much salt does the chef have left? _____

> Practice makes perfect both in dividing decimals and in learning to ride a bike.

Practice Dividing Tenths by Hundredths

Use the model to find the quotient of 0.6 and 0.25.

1. Shade the grid to form a rectangle with an area of 0.6 and a side that measures 0.25.

2. What is the quotient of 0.6 and 0.25? _____

Answer the question.

3. Create and solve a real-world problem that requires dividing 10.5 by 0.75.

    _____

    _____

    _____

    _____

    _____

4. A tree grows 0.35 meter each year. It has grown 2.8 meters since it has been transplanted.

   How many years ago was the tree transplanted? Write and solve a division problem to find out.

   _____

5. The pencils at a store cost $0.65 each. Each pencil weighs 1.85 ounces. All the pencils at the store have a combined weight of 44.4 ounces.

   How much would it cost to buy all the pencils at the store? _____

Divide.

6. $6.8 \div 0.02$ _____

7. $17.1 \div 0.45$ _____

I'm heading to the library to do some math.

8. $4.2 \div 0.24$ _____

9. $15.5 \div 1.25$ _____

Practice Describing the Coordinate System

Answer the question.

1. Draw a coordinate plane so that both axes go from 0 to 5 by ones. Label the axes x and y.

2. Are the axes of a coordinate plane parallel or perpendicular? _____

3. What is the name of the point where the two axes of a coordinate

   plane intersect? _____

Look! It's a coordinate plane.

4. Eloise says, "The coordinate plane has two number 1s, two number 2s, two number 3s, and so on. How can I specify which of the two numbers I'm talking about?"

How would you reply to Eloise?

_____

_____

_____

_____

_____

_____

5. A point has an x-coordinate of 4 and a y-coordinate of 9.

What ordered pair describes the point? _____

6. What ordered pair describes the origin? _____

7. How could a map of a park with a coordinate plane on top of it help a search-and-rescue team find a lost and injured hiker?

_____

_____

_____

_____

_____

_____

Practice Writing Ordered Pairs

Use the graph to answer the questions.

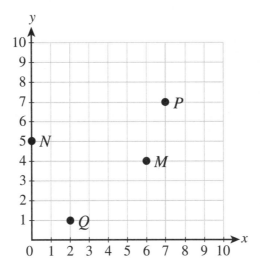

1. Locate point *M*.

   a. What is the *x*-coordinate of point *M*? _____

   b. What is the *y*-coordinate of point *M*? _____

   c. What is the ordered pair for point *M*? _____

2. Locate point *N*.

   a. What is the *x*-coordinate of point *N*? _____

   b. What is the *y*-coordinate of point *N*? _____

   c. What is the ordered pair for point *N*? _____

3. What is the ordered pair for point *P*? _____

4. What is the ordered pair for point *Q*? _____

An archaeologist finds artifacts at the locations shown on the graph. Use the graph to answer the questions.

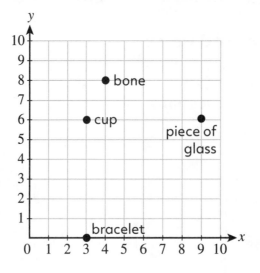

5. What is the ordered pair for the bone? _____

6. What is the ordered pair for the piece of glass? _____

7. What is the ordered pair for the cup? _____

8. What is the ordered pair for the bracelet? _____

9. What does the ordered pair for the cup have in common with the ordered pairs for the bracelet and the piece of glass?

_____

_____

_____

_____

_____

Coordinate System (C)

Practice Graphing Points

The ordered pair for point P is $(4, 2)$.

1. Complete the statement.

   To plot point P, start at the _____. From there, move _____ units

   to the right and then move up _____ units.

2. Plot and label point P on the coordinate plane.

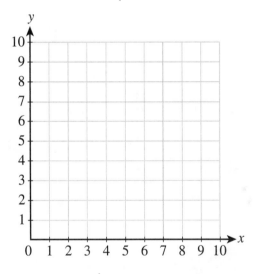

3. Plot and label the points on the coordinate plane in Problem 2.

   a. $Q(0, 7)$

   b. $R(1, 1)$

   c. $S(3, 9)$

   d. $T(9, 5)$

An archaeologist has these coordinates in his field book. Plot and label the points on the coordinate plane.

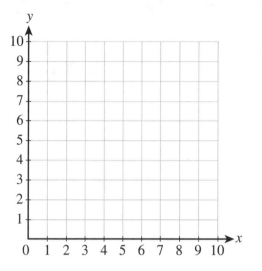

4. coins (6, 3)

5. brick (10, 1)

6. crown (2, 9)

7. tent (5, 0)

8. sword (8, 7)

Coordinate planes are very useful in my archaeological digs.

Problem Solving on the Coordinate Plane (A)

Practice Using the Coordinate Plane

The coordinate plane represents a zoo. The top is north. Each unit is 1 block.

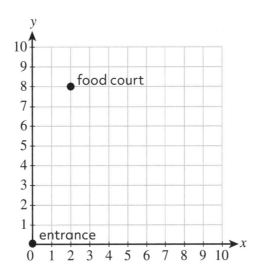

1. The directions from the zoo entrance to the entrances of each of three popular exhibits are given. Write the ordered pair for each location. Then, graph and label the point on the coordinate plane.

   a. monkey exhibit: Go 2 blocks east and 1 block north.

      ordered pair: _____

   b. elephant exhibit: Go 7 blocks east and 6 blocks north.

      ordered pair: _____

   c. polar bear exhibit: Go 5 blocks north.

      ordered pair: _____

2. What could be the directions from the food court to the zoo entrance?

_____

3. Each block is 250 feet long. What is the distance from the entrance of

the monkey exhibit to the food court? _____

Graph the polygons and answer the questions.

4. The vertices of square $ABCD$ are $A(7, 1)$, $B(7, 3)$, $C(9, 3)$, and $D(9, 1)$. Graph and label the vertices on the coordinate plane. Draw the sides of the square.

    a. What is the perimeter of the square? _____

    b. What is the area of the square? _____

5. The vertices of rectangle $MNPQ$ are $M(4, 10)$, $N(4, 0)$, $P(1, 0)$, and $Q(1, 10)$. Graph and label the vertices on the coordinate plane. Draw the sides of the rectangle.

    a. What is the perimeter of the rectangle? _____

    b. What is the area of the rectangle? _____

Problem Solving on the Coordinate Plane (B)

Practice Working with Data on the Coordinate Plane

Matthew and Eloise play a card game 4 times.

1. These ordered pairs show the game number and the number of points Matthew earns in each game.

    $$(1, 4), (2, 0), (3, 3), (4, 2)$$

    To graph the data, draw a coordinate plane, label the axes, and plot the pairs.

2. The table shows how many points each player scores per game. Graph the data on the coordinate plane.

Matthew	Eloise
4	5
0	3
3	1
2	1

Students are asked to identify several plants and animals. The graph shows the number of plants and animals each student correctly identifies.

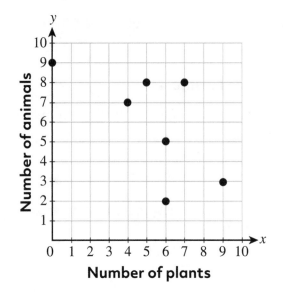

3. Kiki correctly identifies 7 plants. How many animals does she correctly

   identify? _____

4. Min does not identify any plants correctly. How many animals does he

   correctly identify? _____

5. How many students correctly identify 8 animals? _____

6. Aisha correctly identifies the fewest number of animals. How many

   plants does she correctly identify? _____

Problem Solving on the Coordinate Plane (C)

Practice Working with Steady Rates of Change

Eric fills cups of water from a container.

1. The table shows how much water remains after Eric fills each cup. Graph the data on the coordinate plane.

Number of cups	Water remaining (oz)
0	48
1	42
2	36
3	30
4	24
5	18
6	12
7	6
8	0

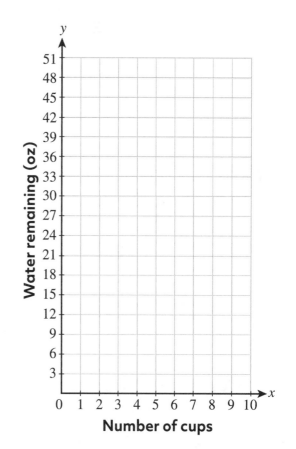

Maria reads the same number of pages in her book each day. Use the graph to answer the questions.

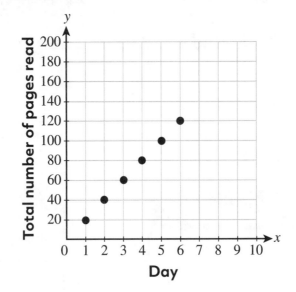

2. On which day does Maria read her 100th page? _____

3. How many pages has Maria read by the end of Day 3? _____

4. How many pages does Maria read each day? _____

5. Maria's book has 180 pages. She continues to read the same number of pages each day.

   On what day does Maria finish the book? _____

Problem Solving on the Coordinate Plane (D)

Practice Working with Number Patterns

Sarah and Juan make number patterns that start at 0.

1. Sarah's pattern is to "add 20." Juan's pattern is to "add 5." Complete each pattern.

Sarah's pattern	0					
Juan's pattern	0					

2. Fill in the blank: Every term in Juan's pattern is _____ times the corresponding term in Sarah's pattern.

3. List the ordered pairs formed from combining the terms in Sarah's pattern with the corresponding term in Juan's pattern.

4. Graph the ordered pairs on the coordinate plane.

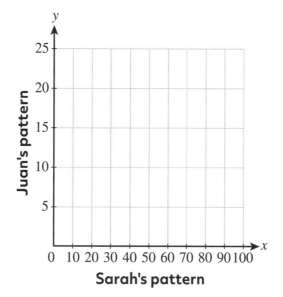

Min and Natalie also make number patterns that start at 0.

5. Min's pattern is to "add 10." Natalie's pattern is to "add 25." Complete each pattern.

Min's pattern	0					
Natalie's pattern	0					

6. Fill in the blank: Every term in Natalie's pattern is _____ times the corresponding term in Min's pattern.

7. List the ordered pairs formed from combining the terms in Min's pattern with the corresponding term in Natalie's pattern.

_____

8. Graph the ordered pairs on the coordinate plane.

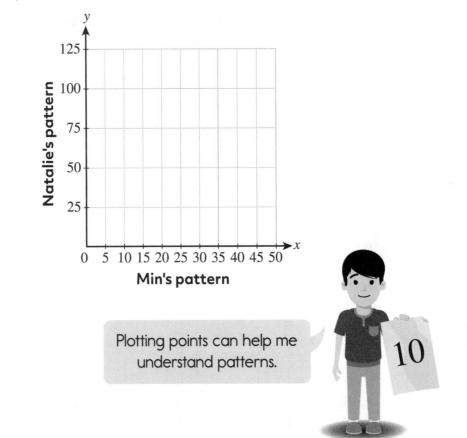

Plotting points can help me understand patterns.

10

Practice Converting Metric Units of Length

Convert.

$$
\begin{aligned}
1 \text{ cm} &= 10 \text{ mm} \\
1 \text{ m} &= 100 \text{ cm} = 1{,}000 \text{ mm} \\
1 \text{ km} &= 1{,}000 \text{ m}
\end{aligned}
$$

1. $7 \text{ m} = $ _____ cm

2. $40{,}000 \text{ m} = $ _____ km

3. $38 \text{ cm} = $ _____ mm

4. $100 \text{ km} = $ _____ m

5. $9.2 \text{ m} = $ _____ mm

6. $116 \text{ mm} = $ _____ cm

7. $49 \text{ mm} = $ _____ m

8. $0.3 \text{ cm} = $ _____ m

9. $88.7 \text{ km} = $ _____ m

10. $2.1 \text{ cm} = $ _____ mm

Answer the question.

11. Matthew finds a rope with a length of 2.8 meters. It is too long, so he cuts it down to 2.5 meters.

    How many centimeters of rope does Matthew cut off? _____

12. It rains 30 millimeters on Tuesday and 0.3 centimeter on Wednesday.

    On which day does it rain more? How much more?

    _____

13. A toy train track is set up in a loop that is 4 meters long. It is estimated that a toy train on this track could complete the loop 500 times on one battery.

    How many kilometers could the toy train travel on one battery? _____

14. Jessica has 40 centimeters of green ribbon and 0.85 meter of purple ribbon.

    How many meters of ribbon does Jessica have in all? _____

> The unit on a measurement helps me understand the size of the measurement.

Using Units of Length (B)

Practice Converting Customary Units of Length

Convert.

> 1 ft = 12 in.
>
> 1 yd = 3 ft = 36 in.
>
> 1 mi = 1,760 yd = 5,280 ft

1. 5 yd = _____ in.

2. 10 mi = _____ yd

3. 144 in. = _____ yd

4. 21 ft = _____ yd

5. $\frac{9}{10}$ mi = _____ ft

6. 45 in. = _____ ft

7. $\frac{1}{4}$ ft = _____ in.

8. 2,640 ft = _____ mi

9. 1.75 yd = _____ in.

10. $\frac{1}{12}$ ft = _____ in.

Answer the question.

11. Eloise's mom wants a tree that is 6 feet tall. She buys a tree that is 69 inches tall.

   How does the height of the tree Eloise's mom buys compare with the height she wants?

   _____

   _____

12. Eric has 126 inches of rope at home. He purchases 20 more yards of rope at the store.

   How many yards of rope does Eric have after his purchase? _____

13. A 10-mile race is divided into 20 equal sections.

   What is the length of each section in feet? _____

14. A playground is rectangular and has a perimeter of 172 feet. It has a width of 12 yards.

   What is the length of the playground in feet? _____

Using Units of Liquid Volume (A)

Practice Converting Metric Units of Liquid Volume

Convert.

$$1\ L = 1{,}000\ mL$$

1. 345 mL = _____ L

2. 6 L = _____ mL

3. 820 mL = _____ L

4. 70,000 mL = _____ L

5. 1.3 L = _____ mL

6. 0.4 L = _____ mL

7. 0.025 L = _____ mL

8. 55 mL = _____ L

9. 0.202 L = _____ mL

10. 1,298 mL = _____ L

Answer the question.

11. Sarah's mom buys a basket that contains 8 bottles of lotion. Half of the bottles each contain 150 milliliters of lotion. The other bottles each contain 175 milliliters of lotion.

    How many liters of lotion does Sarah's mom buy? _____

12. A serving of soup is 275 milliliters.

    Will 6 servings of soup fit into a jar that holds up to 1.5 liters of liquid? Explain.

    _____

    _____

13. The same amount of water drips out of a faucet every day. A total of 1.4 liters drips out every week.

    How many milliliters of water drip out of the faucet every day? _____

14. An artist buys 2 liters of paint for a project. When he is done with the project, he has 350 milliliters of the paint left over. The paint costs 2¢ per milliliter.

    How many dollars' worth of paint does the artist use for the project? _____

Using Units of Liquid Volume (B)

Practice Converting Customary Units of Liquid Volume

Convert.

$$1 \, c = 8 \, \text{fl oz}$$
$$1 \, pt = 2 \, c = 16 \, \text{fl oz}$$
$$1 \, qt = 2 \, pt = 32 \, \text{fl oz}$$
$$1 \, gal = 4 \, qt = 128 \, \text{fl oz}$$

1. 6 pt = _____ c

2. 32 c = _____ qt

3. $3\frac{1}{2}$ c = _____ fl oz

4. 100 gal = _____ qt

5. 8 pt = _____ gal

6. 5 pt = _____ qt

7. $\frac{1}{2}$ qt = _____ fl oz

8. 2 gal = _____ c

9. 100 fl oz = _____ pt

10. $\frac{7}{8}$ gal = _____ fl oz

Answer the question.

11. Juan's mom drinks 1 cup of tea with breakfast, 4 fluid ounces of tea with lunch, and 6 fluid ounces of tea with dinner.

    How many cups of tea does Juan's mom drink? _____

12. A bag holds 100 fluid ounces of water. Evan drains $1\frac{1}{2}$ quarts of water from the bag. Then, Matthew drains another 3 pints of water from the bag.

    How many fluid ounces of water remain in the bag? _____

13. A hotel uses 300 quarts of bleach each month. It pays $1.78 for each gallon of bleach.

    How much does the hotel spend on bleach each month? _____

14. A daycare center starts the day with 5 quarts of milk. At the end of the day, 4 cups of milk remain.

    How many cups of milk do the children drink? _____

Practice Converting Units of Mass

Convert.

$$1 \text{ g} = 1,000 \text{ mg}$$
$$1 \text{ kg} = 1,000 \text{ g}$$

1. 4 g = _____ mg

2. 12,000 g = _____ kg

3. 1,850 mg = _____ g

4. 67 kg = _____ g

5. 36 g = _____ kg

6. 1.7 g = _____ mg

7. 3.95 kg = _____ g

8. 48,500 mg = _____ g

9. 82 g = _____ kg

10. 91.9 g = _____ mg

Answer the question.

11. A cake recipe calls for 125 grams of butter. Juan's dad says they have 0.2 kilogram of butter.

    Do they have enough butter to make the cake? Explain.

    _____

12. Natalie is using one box to ship 10 books to a friend. Each book weighs 810 grams. The box weighs 250 grams. Shipping costs $3.50 per kilogram.

    How much will it cost Natalie to ship the books? _____

13. A factory uses 50 milligrams of red coloring powder in one batch of candle wax.

    How many batches of candle wax can it make with 25 grams of

    red coloring powder? _____

I wonder how many grams this diamond weighs.

14. One carat equals 0.2 gram. A diamond weighs 300 milligrams.

    How many carats does the diamond weigh? _____

15. How could you convert 6.2 kilograms to milligrams?

    _____

    _____

    _____

Using Units of Mass and Weight (B)

Practice Converting Customary Units of Weight

Convert.

$$1 \text{ lb} = 16 \text{ oz}$$
$$1 \text{ T} = 2{,}000 \text{ lb}$$

1. 2 lb = _____ oz

2. 8,000 lb = _____ T

3. 10 T = _____ lb

4. 60 oz = _____ lb

5. $4\frac{1}{2}$ lb = _____ oz

6. $\frac{1}{4}$ T = _____ lb

7. 2 oz = _____ lb

8. 3.2 T = _____ lb

9. $\frac{1}{16}$ lb = _____ oz

10. 1,000 lb = _____ T

Answer the question.

11. A company's shipping policy is that the first 2 pounds of a customer's order ship for free and the remaining weight is charged at a rate of 20¢ per ounce.

    How much will be the shipping for a package weighing 80 ounces? _____

12. A railcar on a train is carrying 120 tons of coal. The coal will sell for 3¢ per pound.

    How much will all the coal on the railcar sell for? _____

13. A cat weighs 11 pounds 4 ounces when the veterinarian tells the owner to put the cat on a special diet until it reaches its target weight.
    The cat's target weight is $2\frac{1}{2}$ pounds less than its current weight.

    What is the cat's target weight, in pounds and ounces? _____

14. An employee at a plant nursery is given a 5-pound bag of potting mix and told to put 6 ounces of potting mix into each of the small pots.

    How many small pots could the employee fill completely?

    How many ounces are left over? _____

Customary Units and Line Plots (A)

Practice Representing Data on a Line Plot

The data set shows the amount of rain, in inches, recorded in nearby cities from a storm.

$$3, 2\frac{1}{4}, 2\frac{3}{4}, 2, 2\frac{1}{2}, 2\frac{1}{2}, 2\frac{1}{2}, 2\frac{3}{4}, 2, 3, 2, 2\frac{3}{4}, 2\frac{1}{2}, 2\frac{1}{2}, 2\frac{3}{4}$$

1. How many times does each value occur?

   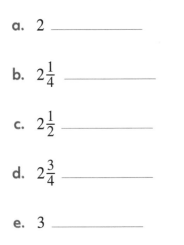

   a. 2 _____

   b. $2\frac{1}{4}$ _____

   c. $2\frac{1}{2}$ _____

   d. $2\frac{3}{4}$ _____

   e. 3 _____

2. Complete the line plot for the amounts of rain.

   Rainfall in Different Cities

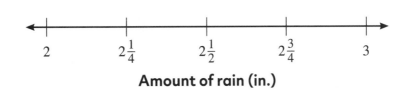

Amount of rain (in.)

Create a line plot for the data set.

3. Lengths of roller coasters, in miles:

$$\frac{7}{8}, \frac{5}{8}, \frac{1}{2}, 1, 1\frac{1}{4}, \frac{1}{2}, \frac{5}{8}, 1\frac{1}{8}, \frac{3}{4}, 1, \frac{5}{8}, \frac{1}{2}, \frac{5}{8}, \frac{7}{8}$$

4. Weights of parrots, in pounds:

$$7\frac{1}{2}, 4\frac{1}{2}, 5, 6\frac{1}{2}, 8, 4, 5\frac{1}{2}, 7\frac{1}{2}, 5, 7\frac{1}{2}, 5\frac{1}{2}, 6\frac{1}{2}, 7$$

Customary Units and Line Plots (B)

Practice Interpreting a Line Plot

Answer the questions.

1. The line plot shows the weights of the cars in Eric's toy car collection, rounded to the nearest quarter of an ounce.

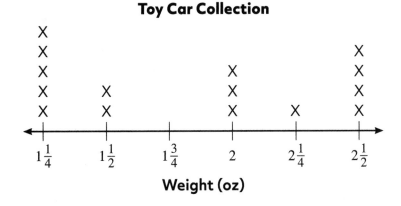

Toy Car Collection

Weight (oz)

a. What is the difference between the weight of the heaviest car

and the weight of the lightest car? _____

b. Eric chooses one car of each weight to display on his top shelf.

What is the total weight of the cars on his top shelf? _____

c. A small figurine weighs $\frac{2}{5}$ the weight of one of the lightest cars in Eric's collection.

How much does the figurine weigh? _____

2. The line plot shows the amount of oil that an auto mechanic adds to the engines of 10 cars in one day.

Oil Added to Engines

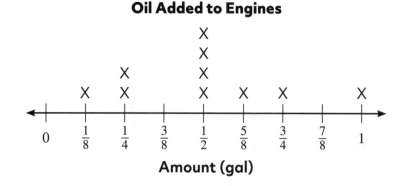

Amount (gal)

a. Natalie's dad's car needs the same amount of oil that is added to most of the engines that day. The mechanic adds the oil by pouring the same amount into the engine 4 times.

How much oil does the mechanic add to the engine each time? _____

b. What is the total amount of oil that the mechanic adds to all the engines? _____

c. Suppose the total amount of oil added to all the engines is divided so that the mechanic adds the same amount of oil to each engine.

How much oil would the mechanic have added to each engine? _____

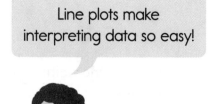

Line plots make interpreting data so easy!

Practice Classifying Triangles by Angle Measures

Fill in the blanks to complete the statement.

1. Every triangle is a polygon that has _____ side(s) and _____ angle(s).

2. Every triangle can be classified by its angles into one of three categories:

   _____ triangle, _____ triangle, or _____ triangle.

3. Every acute triangle has _____ acute angle(s), _____ obtuse angle(s),

   and _____ right angle(s).

4. Every right triangle has _____ acute angle(s), _____ obtuse angle(s),

   and _____ right angle(s).

5. Every obtuse triangle has _____ acute angle(s), _____ obtuse angle(s),

   and _____ right angle(s).

Fill in the chart.

6. If the statement applies to the category of triangles, place an X in the box. If not, leave the box blank.

Statement	Acute triangle	Right triangle	Obtuse triangle
The triangle is a polygon.			
The triangle has 3 sides.			
The triangle has 3 acute angles.			

Statement	Acute triangle	Right triangle	Obtuse triangle
The triangle has 2 acute angles.			
The triangle has 1 right angle.			
The triangle has 1 obtuse angle.			

Use the flag to answer the questions.

7. Fill in the blanks to complete the statement about the angle measures in the triangle.

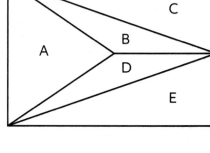

a. Triangle A has _____ acute angle(s), _____ obtuse angle(s), and _____ right angle(s).

b. Triangle B has _____ acute angle(s), _____ obtuse angle(s), and _____ right angle(s).

c. Triangle C has _____ acute angle(s), _____ obtuse angle(s), and _____ right angle(s).

d. Triangle D has _____ acute angle(s), _____ obtuse angle(s), and _____ right angle(s).

e. Triangle E has _____ acute angle(s), _____ obtuse angle(s), and _____ right angle(s).

8. Write the letter(s) of the triangles from the flag in the classification to which they belong.

Acute triangle	Right triangle	Obtuse triangle

Practice Classifying Triangles by Side Lengths

Fill in the blanks to complete the statement.

1. Every triangle is a polygon that has _____ side(s) and _____ angle(s).

2. Every triangle can be classified by its sides into one of three categories:

   _____ triangle, _____ triangle, or _____ triangle.

3. Every equilateral triangle has _____ side(s) with equal lengths and is always

   an _____ triangle.

4. Every isosceles triangle has _____ side(s) with equal lengths and could be an acute,

   _____, or obtuse triangle.

5. Every scalene triangle has _____ side(s) with equal lengths and could be

   an _____, right, or obtuse triangle.

Fill in the chart.

6. If the triangle fits in both categories, place an X in the box. If not, leave the box blank.

Side classification	Acute triangle	Right triangle	Obtuse triangle
equilateral triangle			
isosceles triangle			
scalene triangle			

Use the flag to answer the questions.

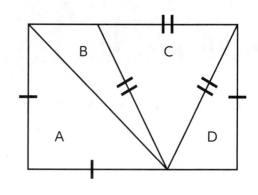

7. Fill in the blank to complete the statement about the side lengths of the triangle.

a. Triangle A has _____ side lengths that are equal in length.

b. Triangle B has _____ side lengths that are equal in length.

c. Triangle C has _____ side lengths that are equal in length.

d. Triangle D has _____ side lengths that are equal in length.

8. Write the letter(s) of the triangles from the flag in the classification to which they belong. A triangle may be classified in more than one way.

Scalene triangle	Isosceles triangle	Equilateral triangle

Sketch the triangle.

9. a right scalene triangle

10. an isosceles only triangle

11. an equilateral triangle

Practice Classifying Polygons

Fill in the blanks to complete the statement.

1. A hexagon is a polygon with _____ sides and _____ angles.

2. A quadrilateral is a polygon with _____ sides and _____ angles.

3. A pentagon is a polygon with _____ sides and _____ angles.

4. A triangle is a polygon with _____ sides and _____ angles.

5. The polygons from Problems 1–4 in order from fewest number of sides to most number of sides are _____ .

Fill in the chart.

6. Classify the polygon by the number of sides.

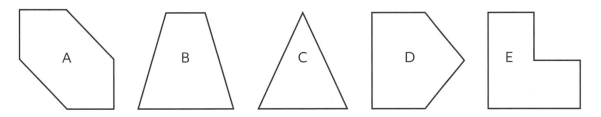

Hexagon	Pentagon	Quadrilateral	Triangle

Classify the polygon.

7. _____

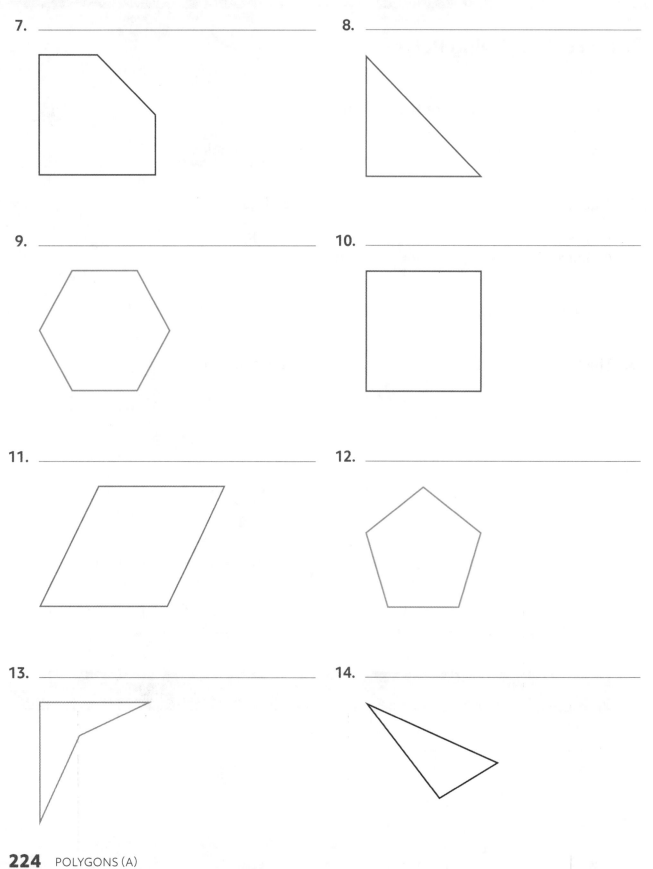

8. _____

9. _____

10. _____

11. _____

12. _____

13. _____

14. _____

Polygons (B)

Practice Describing and Classifying Quadrilaterals

Complete the flowchart with the names of the polygons.

1.

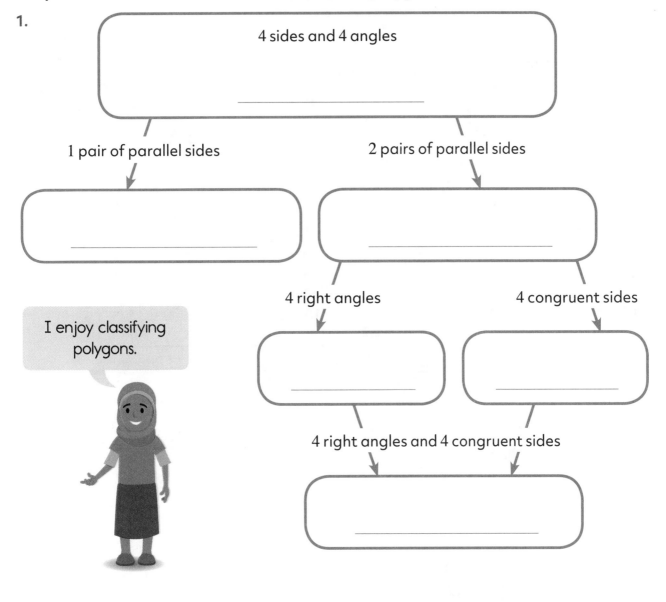

4 sides and 4 angles

_____

1 pair of parallel sides

_____

2 pairs of parallel sides

_____

I enjoy classifying polygons.

4 right angles

_____

4 congruent sides

_____

4 right angles and 4 congruent sides

_____

Answer the question.

2. I have 4 sides. What shape am I? _____

3. I have 4 right angles and 4 congruent sides. What shape am I? _____

4. I have 2 pairs of parallel sides. My side lengths are all equal.

   I have no right angles. What shape am I? _____

5. I have exactly 1 pair of parallel sides. What shape am I? _____

6. I have 2 pairs of parallel sides and 4 right angles. What shape am I? _____

Classify the polygon.

7. _____

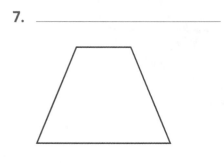

8. _____

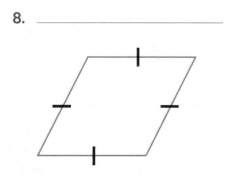

9. _____

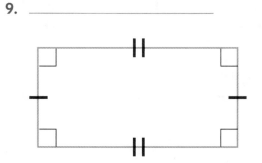

10. _____

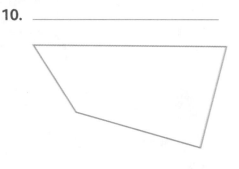

11. _____

12. _____

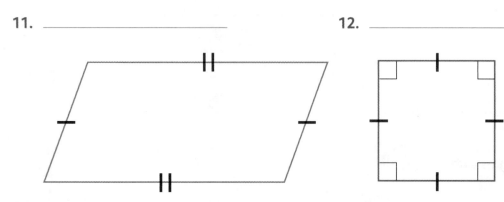

Glossary

acute angle – an angle that measures greater than 0° and less than 90°

acute triangle – a triangle with 3 acute angles

algorithm – a step-by-step way to solve a problem

area – the amount of space on a flat surface, most often measured in square units

area model – a model for multiplication that shows the product of two factors as the total number of squares on a rectangular grid; one factor is the number of rows and the other factor is the number of columns

array – a pattern of objects or numbers placed in a rectangular formation of rows and columns

base – the number repeatedly multiplied when the number has an exponent

benchmark number – a number that can be used to compare or estimate other numbers; whole numbers and halves are common benchmark numbers

centimeter (cm) – a metric unit used to measure length; 1 centimeter $= \frac{1}{100}$ of a meter

compatible numbers – numbers that are easy to compute using mental math

composite number – a whole number greater than 1 that is not prime

composite solid – a solid composed, or made up, of more than one solid

coordinate (on a number line) – the number associated with a point on a number line

coordinate (on the coordinate plane) – a location on the coordinate plane, designated by an x-value and a y-value

coordinate plane – a plane on which points can be located that has an x-axis and a y-axis perpendicular to each other

cubed – the result of the operation where a number has been multiplied by itself two times, such as 5 cubed $= 5^3 = 5 \times 5 \times 5 = 125$; when the volume of a cube is found, the dimensions are cubed, and the volume is expressed in units cubed

cubic centimeter – a cube that is 1 cm on each side; a measure of volume

cubic foot – a cube that is 1 ft on each side; a measure of volume

cubic inch – a cube that is 1 in. on each side; a measure of volume

cubic unit – a cube that is 1 unit on each side; a measure of volume

cup (c) – a unit for measuring capacity in the English system of measurement; 1 c $= 8$ fl oz

data – numerical information that has been gathered

decimal number – a number written with a decimal point; sometimes called a decimal fraction

decimal place value – one of the place values that follow the decimal point in a number, such as tenths or thousandths

decimal point – the point in a decimal number that separates a whole number from the decimal (or fraction) part

degree – a unit used to measure angles

denominator – the number in a fraction that is below the fraction bar

difference – the answer to a subtraction problem

dividend – the number to be divided; the dividend divided by the divisor equals the quotient

divisor – the number that divides the dividend; the dividend divided by the divisor equals the quotient

equilateral triangle – a triangle that has all sides equal in length

equivalent fractions – fractions that name the same amount, such as $\frac{1}{2}$ and $\frac{3}{6}$

equivalent triangle – a triangle that has all sides equal in length

estimate (v.) – to make a very good guess or rough calculation of an answer when the exact answer is not necessary

evaluate – to find the value of an expression

expanded form – a way to write a number that shows the place value of each of its digits; for example, $543 = 500 + 40 + 3$ or 5 hundreds + 4 tens + 3 ones

exponent – the number of times a base number is multiplied by itself

expression – one or more numbers and symbols that show a certain value, such as $2 + 3$, or $3 \times ?$, or $10 - 4 + 1$

factor – one of two or more numbers that are multiplied

factor pairs – two numbers that multiply to give a particular product; factor pairs of 6 are 6×1 and 3×2

foot (ft) – the English, or customary, unit for measuring length that equals 12 in.

fraction – a number that represents a part of a whole or a part of a set

gallon (gal) – the English, or customary, unit for measuring capacity that equals 128 fl oz or 4 qt

gram (g) – the basic metric unit of mass

greater-than symbol (>) – a symbol that shows that one amount is greater than another

greatest common factor (GCF) – the greatest whole number that is a factor of two or more given whole numbers

grouping symbols – symbols used to set numbers or expressions apart, such as parentheses

hexagon – a 6-sided polygon

hour (h) – the unit for measuring time that equals 60 min

hundredths – the place value immediately to the right of the tenths place; 10 thousandths = 1 hundredth and 10 hundredths = 1 tenth

improper fraction – a fraction whose numerator is greater than or equal to its denominator

inch (in.) – the basic English, or customary, unit for measuring length

intersecting lines – lines that cross at one point or at all points

inverse operations – opposite operations that undo each other; subtraction and addition are inverse operations; division and multiplication are inverse operations

inverse relationship – the relationship between operations that reverse or undo each other; addition and subtraction have an inverse relationship; multiplication and division have an inverse relationship

isosceles triangle – a triangle that has at least 2 sides equal in length; an equilateral triangle is a special type of isosceles triangle

kilogram (kg) – the metric unit for measuring mass that equals 1,000 g

kilometer (km) – the metric unit for measuring distance that equals 1,000 m

least common denominator (LCD) – the least common multiple of two or more denominators

least common multiple (LCM) – the least number, other than 0, that is a multiple of two or more given whole numbers; used for the least common denominator

less-than symbol (<) – a symbol that shows that one amount is less than another

like denominators – denominators that are exactly the same in two or more fractions

line – a straight path of points that goes on forever in both directions

line plot – number line that shows all the pieces of data with a mark or marks above each piece of data to show how many times that piece of data occurred

line segment – a straight path of points that has endpoints at both ends; also called a segment

line symmetry – a type of symmetry where a plane figure can have a line or lines drawn through it so that one half is the mirror image of the other half; when the figure is folded along a line of symmetry, one half must fit exactly onto the other half

liter (L) – the basic metric unit of volume; 1 L = 1,000 mL

mass – the amount of matter in an object; the amount of mass remains the same no matter where the object is, but the weight of an object can change depending on the pull of gravity on the object

meter (m) – the basic metric unit for measuring length

milliliter (mL) – the metric unit for measuring capacity that equals $\frac{1}{1,000}$ L

minute (min) – the unit for measuring time that equals 60 s

mixed number – a whole number and a proper fraction that show a single amount

multiple – the product of a given number and any whole number

multiplication fact family – a set of four related multiplication and division facts that use the same set of three numbers

numerator – the number in a fraction that is above the fraction bar

obtuse angle – an angle that measures greater than 90° and less than 180°

obtuse triangle – a triangle with 1 angle greater than 90°

order of operations – a set of rules that tells the correct order to use to solve a problem that has more than one operation

ordered pair – a pair of numbers that names the location of a point

origin – the coordinate (0, 0) on a coordinate plane

ounce (oz) – the basic English, or customary, unit for measuring weight as $\frac{1}{16}$ lb and capacity as $\frac{1}{8}$ c

parallel lines – lines in the same flat surface that never intersect

parallelogram – a quadrilateral with two pairs of parallel sides

partial product – the product of each place value when a multidigit factor is multiplied by a single-digit or multidigit factor; the sum of the partial products is the final product for the problem

pentagon – a 5-sided polygon

perimeter – the distance around the edge of a shape

perpendicular lines – lines that intersect and form angles that measure 90°

pint (pt) – the English, or customary, unit for measuring capacity that equals 16 fl oz or 2 c

place value – the value of a digit depending on its position, or place, in a number

place-value chart – a chart that shows the value of each digit in a number

point – a location in space

polygon – a plane shape made of 3 or more straight sides that separate the inside of the shape from the outside

pound (lb) – the English, or customary, unit for measuring weight that equals 16 oz

power – a product in which all the factors are the same; for example, 16 is the fourth power of 2, because $2 \times 2 \times 2 \times 2 = 16$

power of 10 – a number that can be written as a power with a base of 10

prime factorization – an expression showing a whole number as a product of its prime factors

prime number – a whole number greater than 1 that has only two whole-number factors, 1 and itself

product – the answer to a multiplication problem

proper fraction – a fraction in which the numerator is less than the denominator

protractor – a tool to measure the degrees in an angle

quadrilateral – a 4-sided polygon

quart (qt) – the English, or customary, unit for measuring capacity that equals 32 fl oz or 2 pt

quotient – the answer to a division problem; the dividend divided by the divisor equals the quotient

ray – a straight path of points that has an endpoint at one end and goes on forever from that endpoint

reciprocal – two numbers whose product is 1

rectangle – a parallelogram with four 90° angles; a square is a special type of rectangle

rectangular prism – a solid figure with six faces that are rectangles

reflex angle – an angle that measures greater than 180° and less than 360°

remainder – the amount left over after dividing evenly

rhombus (plural: rhombuses) – a parallelogram that has all sides equal in length; a square is a special type of rhombus

right angle – an angle that measures exactly 90°

right triangle – a triangle with a right angle

round (v.) – to change a number to the nearest place value asked in a problem; for example, rounding 532 to the nearest ten would be 530

scalene triangle – a triangle that has no sides equal in length

second – the basic unit for measuring time

simplest form – of fractions, a fraction with a numerator and denominator that have no common factor other than 1

solid figure – a figure with three dimensions: length, width, and height or depth

square – a parallelogram that has all sides equal in length and four 90° angles

standard form – the usual way of writing a number using digits

straight angle – an angle that measures exactly 180°; a straight angle is a line

tenths – the place value immediately to the right of the ones place after the decimal; 10 hundredths = 1 tenth and 10 tenths = 1

term in a pattern – each number or object in a pattern

thousandths – the place value immediately to the right of the hundredths place after the decimal; 10 thousandths = 1 hundredth

ton – the English, or customary, unit for measuring weight that equals 2,000 lb

trapezoid – a quadrilateral with exactly one pair of parallel sides

triangle – a 3-sided polygon

unit fraction – a fraction with a numerator of 1, such as $\frac{1}{3}$ or $\frac{1}{7}$

unlike denominators – denominators that are different in two or more fractions

vertex (plural: vertices) – the common endpoint of two rays that form an angle

volume – the amount of space taken up by a three-dimensional object; measured in cubic units

weight – the measure of how heavy an object is, such as 10 lb

whole numbers – zero and the counting numbers (0, 1, 2, 3, 4, 5, 6, and so on)

x-axis – the horizontal axis on a coordinate plane, perpendicular to the y-axis

x-coordinate – the first value in an ordered pair, such as 5 in the ordered pair (5, 6)

y-axis – the vertical axis on a coordinate plane, perpendicular to the x-axis

y-coordinate – the second value in an ordered pair, such as 6 in the ordered pair (5, 6)

yard (yd) – the English, or customary, unit for measuring length that equals 36 in. or 3 ft